Circle of the Soul

Anne Carroll Decker

❖ VERITAS PRESS Ltd.

Circle of the Soul

©2001 by Anne Carroll Decker

Library of Congress Control Number 2001 135509

ISBN 0-9652504-1-5

Manufactured in the United States of America
October 2001
First Edition

Published by

 **VERITAS PRESS Ltd.**
PO Box 270735
West Hartford CT 06127-0735
VeritasLtd@aol.com

Produced by
PPC BOOKS
Redington Shores FL

Circle of the Soul

Chapter One

Walk into the Unknown

I hadn't seen the Archangel in seven months and had begun to believe that I would never see him again.

The warm morning sun filtered through the windows as I settled down on the couch. Tucking my feet beneath me, I closed my eyes and quietly began to pray. Within my mind I visualized the expansive beach where I had first met the Archangel. During the last few months it had been empty except for the sounds of the roaring waves and cawing seagulls.

But today—my heart leapt.

At the far end of the barren beach, near a large protruding rock, stood the Archangel. His bronze robes flowed softly in the breeze, yet his blond cascading hair did not move. Although he was yards from me, his tall figure seemed to encompass the beach. In his hand was the familiar golden staff, crooked like a shepherd's hook, with the sign of an x encrusted in jewels. Knowing that the staff contained the gifts of God, I caught my breath. Stepping into the scene as if into a 3-D movie, I hurried toward the angel, feeling the hot sands beneath my feet.

He smiled, yet remained still.

"I thought you wouldn't return," I said, running toward him. "You said that I was supposed to find God on my own."

"You have prayed and God has sent me."

"Thank you," I said quietly, finally arriving at his side.

"Do not thank me," he said, his voice soft and warm. "Thank the Lord who has sent me. The Lord has heard your prayers and sent me to intercede and help you. Your prayers were constant and calling. I am here to help you find Him."

I looked up to the Archangel, who was easily twice my height. I had missed him desperately, wondering at first why he had visited me and then why he had abruptly left. Months ago he had appeared to me for ten weeks, given me spiritual messages, and told me to "let them be known." Initially I was hesitant to tell anyone of these apparitions. But the messages had so profoundly changed my life that I felt compelled to share them with others. Eventually prayer groups started around New England using photocopies of the manuscript, *Songs of the Soul,* which I subsequently published in book form.

"I am here to speak of the community of the Spirit, the community of the physical, and the community of prayer. All are essential for salvation. The first is the wisdom of knowing God, the second is the action which results from that, and the way to all of this is through the community of prayer. Prayer results in the communication of the spiritual and the physical."

I swallowed hard. I had expected at least a "Hello, how are you?" Struggling to understand his words, I leaned closer to him. Perhaps I was hoping that the crashing of the waves would lessen and I'd hear—or really, understand—the meaning of his monologue.

"Remember this," he said, "and write it down. All of it is essential."

"Wait a minute," I said. "I can't write down things I don't even understand."

"You will understand this shortly, and begin to live it."

I dug my toes into the warm sand, keeping my eyes locked on his face. "I haven't done a very good job, have I?" I asked, knowing that my faith constantly wavered. My doubts were always haunting me. I stared at the Archangel's face. A glow permeated his figure; a warm golden light encircled his body. His large wings flickered slightly as he moved.

"You have not walked into the unknown with faith," he said.

"I don't understand."

"You must walk into the unknown with faith. That is where you are stumbling. It is difficult for you to accept the gifts because you are still lacking true faith. As Peter walked on the water toward Christ, and then doubted and fell, so do you. And with each doubt you fall into the sea, swim back to shore, and begin again. You must live your faith."

"That's not as easy as you make it sound," I said, biting and tugging at my cuticles.

His wings rustled behind him. "In the beginning," he said, "you did not need faith. You were one with God and saw Him. Then you turned from the Light. Now the challenge is to move toward Him without seeing clearly."

"Without seeing clearly?"

"It is as simple as that. Your vision is blurred, but God is there. Push aside the silken cobwebs that block your view. He is there. Your faith will allow you to see this. Your faith will allow you to accept the gifts which surround you."

I knew the gifts he was speaking about. During his last visit he had handed me a variety of gems, representing serenity, grace, comfort, and others. I, like many people, had had trouble holding tightly to the jewels. "But," I said, stammering and close to tears, "why does it seem so difficult?"

"Because you cannot see clearly. Your road seems blurred and comfort calls from the apparent. But the truly present is within your grasp. Reach for it in faith. Move toward God in prayer. See with your soul, not your eyes."

"I'm not trying hard enough, am I?" I said desperately.

"No," he answered with a smile. "You are trying too hard. Walk in faith; it is much easier. Do not question the events that occur. Do not dissect everything intellectually. Let your soul soar with the Word. Let your soul listen to the call."

"But *how*?" I asked. "I have to know *how*. It's not as easy as you say." A warm ocean breeze touched my face as I stood there, waiting for an explanation, waiting to understand why I didn't just "walk in faith."

The Archangel shook his head. "Breathe in the Spirit. Just as the air of the world supports your body, so does the Holy Spirit support your soul. Energy moves both. And fear halts both. Disease is the blocking of energy meant to support your body. When the energy goes awry, illness begins to grow. Such is the energy of the soul. When the energy is not allowed to flow simply, as it was meant to, doubt and illness arise."

"What do you mean, 'meant to'?"

"Have we not told you many times how simple this is? Yet your mind and body dissect everything, trying to take control of your destiny. Let your spirit guide your destiny. Let your soul soar towards God as it should. Many have not been living in faith. In faith the energy of God moves in the direction it is meant to go. It flows simply in faith and love, supporting and nourishing every part of the soul. But as you turn toward darkness and doubt, the energy becomes stagnant and blocked, and changes course. Redirect the energy. Do not worry about worldly goods; do not worry about matters that do not interest the soul. The soul must be nourished."

I was tired, but I needed to know more answers. "Are you going to say that prayer is the answer? Because sometimes I just can't pray. I try, but the words seem empty."

"Prayer is the answer," he said, folding his hands together. "No prayers are ever empty. Prayer brings faith, and all the gifts are fully experienced. The gifts are for all, but you must take hold of them with faith and hold fast."

I thought back to all the doubts I had had since the Archangel had disappeared, all my apprehensions at "sharing the message." Even a friend of mine had told me I needed to reread *Songs of the Soul* because I had misplaced my gifts. My answer was that I hadn't misplaced them; I had put them in my pocket and they had slipped through a hole. A human condition.

"Come with me," the Archangel said, extending his large hand.

I reached for it. Now I felt secure being with him, unlike many of the visits before. Initially I had worried I might be losing my sanity. But with time his messages took root within my soul, and even more importantly in the souls of those I shared them with. People were praying for their enemies, listening to the message that *None will be saved until all are saved.*

With my fingers wrapped around the Archangel's, I was quickly transported to a glass-enclosed arcade lined with doors of shops. Without needing to ask, I knew the shops were bookstores. I had seen this corridor once before, and I knew that more lessons awaited me through the doors.

Gripping the Archangel's hand, I said, "You told me these stores are for future lessons, after I had learned the other lessons. I haven't even learned a portion of what I'm supposed to. I still have a hard time praying for my enemy, realizing that we are one."

Keeping my small hand in his, he shook his head. His angular face was illuminated by radiance beyond description. "You have prayed, and although you have much to learn, you are ready to see more. Each day you realize that you are not alone on this journey. You are all one. And to help you learn more, God has allowed me to return and show you more knowledge, more wisdom."

"Will this knowledge finally help me find peace?" I asked, knowing that my doubts and anxieties always seemed to win out over any times of spiritual tranquility.

The Archangel turned very somber. "The peace you are searching for is only with God. I can help you on the path, I can pray for you and guide you, but finally, the decision is with you. It is your decision to find peace with God."

I didn't say anything, but at his urging I pushed the glass door gently with my palm, knowing that a new leg of my journey had begun.

Chapter Two

Take Hold of Your Destiny

The door swung open and the Book Keeper, whom I immediately recognized, greeted me. He sat on a tall stool in the center of this circular room. Ancient books covered the walls, towering from floor to ceiling. Only the doorway was free of the paneled bookshelves.

I turned toward the Archangel, but he was gone. The lone monk and I remained in the room. Stepping cautiously toward the middle, I nodded to the cassock-clad man. He pointed toward a book. The volume lay on a wooden lectern in the center of the room. It was bound in rich burgundy leather. As I touched it I noticed many of the pages were torn, almost disintegrating with age. I brushed layers of dust from them.

"Be careful," he said slowly. "It is precarious."

"The book?"

He barely looked up. "The contents."

I didn't understand, but turned a golden-edged page.

"The Energy of the Soul," I read aloud. I held the book tightly in my hands, afraid to continue.

"Do not be afraid," the Book Keeper said, obviously knowing my thoughts. "Didn't the Archangel tell you to step out in faith? Is your lack of faith keeping you from living?"

"Keeping me from living? I'm living all right," I said, miffed at his attitude. After all, I had a nice family and good friends and was a regular churchgoer.

"I think not," he said, "You are sustaining your life, as if on a life support. You are not living life to its fullest."

"Sure I am."

He shook his head, his gray beard moving against his cheek. "You have not found the peace of God because you are still fearful. That fearfulness permeates your body and your soul. The energy is trapped and clogs your being. Allow it to move."

He pointed toward the book. "You do not need me. You need to face your fears and doubts. Most importantly, face your faith. Move toward God."

My hand remained on the page as my mind raced. Months ago I had been afraid that these messages were figments of my imagination, or that I had been losing my mind. Now I accepted them without question. My entire life had changed, far more than it could have with anything I had invented myself. The messages were beyond my most fertile imagination, and in many cases not edicts I necessarily wanted to follow.

Now, on this second leg of the journey, the visions were not in question nor was my sanity. Actually *living* the messages had become the difficult part.

Slowly I turned the pages, seeing characters and letters I did not understand. Touching a page, I hoped it would turn into something more recognizable, something more legible. Instead I heard the Archangel's voice.

"Pray," he said. "Take hold of your destiny and pray. Let your faith carry you to places you have never dreamed of, peace you have never envisioned, and love you have never imagined. Faith will do that. It will unlock the characters."

I looked around for him but could not see him. "But," I said adamantly, my eyes still searching, "that's the whole problem. *I don't have it!* Can't you see that?"

"It is there for the taking, " he continued. "But you must walk into it. Faith will bring you on an incredible journey. This faith will allow you to travel within your soul."

"Within my soul?"

"Let your soul soar. There is much to experience and you have barely touched the surface. You cannot imagine it. Redirect the energy."

"How?" I had stopped looking for the source of the voice. The Archangel had reappeared in front of me, his robes navy blue and gold. "Listen to your soul. Each day it tells you what it needs to be nourished. Prayer, good works, kindness. Love of God. The soul, when nourished, grows in depth. It moves nearer to the Lord. Allow it that. Break the shell which covers it and redirect the energy." He paused, pressing his hands together in prayer. "Pray to the Holy Spirit. He will give you knowledge and forgiveness. He will breathe into your soul the breath of freedom and wisdom."

Shaking my head, I felt overwhelmed. "I'm sorry. I'm so sorry. But I don't understand any of this. There's energy in my soul?"

"Your soul is perfect. Everything it needs to flourish is there, all the knowledge, all the love. But there is energy around it that you have misdirected. You have locked up your soul."

"You showed me that armor, that shell before," I said, remembering vividly the hard, scratched plastic case that covered my soul. It had appeared almost impenetrable, a defense I had built up over the years.

"Yes," he said, his face almost expressionless. "But now understand the lesson of energy. Energy surrounds everything. Everyone is energy. It must flow. You must flow. You must accept the gifts of God. Flow freely with the spirit of love."

"I've tried to hold fast to those gifts," I said, ashamed. "But sometimes it is difficult."

"There are many gifts, many of which you do not recognize."

I leaned slightly against the lectern, feeling tired and weak. "Such as?"

"Occurrences and people that enter your life are gifts from God."

"Wait a minute," I said, getting my energy back and standing straighter. "Even bad people? My friend got mugged. Don't tell me that's a gift from God." I didn't say it, but I wanted to add, "Spare me from such gifts."

"There are lessons for each of you in these meetings. Learn the

9

lessons. Let the lessons come to you. Do not fight them. You will be helped, as will the others, through prayer. Flow with the energy of love." He paused and moved—or rather, glided—toward the shelves. "When you block out this positive energy, you block out the lessons. You are fighting the pathway. And fear begins to override everything. Let the energy of love flow. When this energy flows, fear cannot exist." He turned back to me, his face awash in a light yellow radiance. "Miracles will happen."

I had forgotten how frustrating our conversations often were. "Easy for you to say," I told him, trying to be respectful. "But you can't just let life flow. There have to be confrontations. You have to take different turns, move in different directions."

"Yes," he answered.

I rubbed my temples. Obviously I was truly lost. "That's not what you said."

"I said," he replied, his voice strong and firm, "to flow with the positive energy of love. Listen to your soul. The pathway is not straight and narrow. There are many curves, many detours, but there are never stops. *There are never stops.* When you stop loving, that is when you misdirect your energy. When you fear, that is when you misdirect your love. Life is flowing; your soul wants constantly to move toward God. When you stop this movement, fear engulfs you."

I sighed and leaned back. My head ached and seemed to spin and I found myself questioning my sanity all over again.

"Do not try to understand all of this now. It will take root in you later." The Archangel smiled and nodded. "It will take root," he repeated with certainty.

I wasn't so sure. "May I go now?" I asked quietly.

"Go with peace," he said, raising his hand and touching my head. "Learn to walk in faith and face the Lord in comfort."

"Thank you," I said, swallowing hard and feeling drained.

Afterwards, while I transcribed my experience, as happened many times before a Voice continued to dictate. I had been wondering about this "energy" which was around our souls, this energy of love, which flowed toward God. I wondered why I misdirected my energy, stopped it, and continually doubted and worried.

The Voice answered as my fingers tapped the keys. "In order for a crop to grow healthy and strong, the farmer must feed the soil. Minerals must nourish the earth; water must quench the thirst of the dry ground. The sun shines, the rains pour down, and the crop thrives. Without such care, the crop may not grow. The seed will remain there, but the crop will not mature to its full potential. Such is the energy surrounding this growth. Such is the energy surrounding your soul. The seed is always there, the potential is always present, yet you must nourish your soul. Prayer is this nourishment."

I interrupted the Voice, stopped typing, and mentally asked. "Can't you just *give* me this faith?"

The Archangel appeared within my mind, shaking his head with a smile. He continued where the Voice had left off. "Then it would not be faith. It is faith and prayer that bring you back to God. Faith nourishes your soul, allowing it to journey, grow, and become one with God. In the beginning faith was not necessary. You saw, but did not value the beauty. Now faith is bringing you back to the beauty of God. Faith is essential for your development."

I sighed. "But it's so difficult to walk blindly."

"It is so simple," he said, contradicting me. "Pray softly, listen to God's whispers to your soul, and step out in love. Step toward God and one another on this road of faith."

I turned off my computer. I wondered if these messages wouldn't wear me out, exhaust me. Yet I knew that deep within me, they were feeding a part of me that was hungry, starved for more information. It was as if I were searching for nourishment, yet all I needed to do was ask and ample food was waiting for me.

Why, I wondered, was the "asking" so difficult?

Chapter Three

Hardship

Each morning after my husband had gone to work, I would set aside a time for prayer. This winter day, not knowing if the Archangel would return or not, I closed my eyes and blocked out the light snow which was falling against the windowpane.

Within seconds I found myself facing a corridor of bookstores in a glass arcade building. My steps echoed against the white tile floor as I pushed open a heavy wooden door.

The Archangel greeted me. "You are learning," he said, "where you need to go for knowledge."

"I am?" I answered, surprised. It seemed just coincidental that I walked into this particular bookstore.

"Prayer shows you the pathway," he said, extending his hand to me. The room was dome-shaped, the ceiling made of stained glass. Rows of bookshelves covered this room too. The Archangel removed a book from a shelf and opened it. Moving closer, I craned my neck to see the contents. The chapter was titled Hardship.

"Hardship," I read, anticipating a list of horrible events.

"You bring all hardship on yourselves," the Archangel said, turning the first page of the chapter. The pages were blank.

"No, no," I said, shaking my head. "The world is full of hardship." I looked upward at the angel's clear blue eyes, trying to get through to him. "Think of all the atrocities of life. A mother discovers her son shot dead in a convenience store, murdered for a few dollars. A husband is killed, his wife raped while burglars ransack their home. People discover they have terminal illnesses." My voice got louder with each injustice I vocalized. "There are so many, it would take eternity to speak of them all."

The Archangel's expression didn't change. His eyes remained calm, focused, yet warm. "The body has limited time; the soul is eternal. In those cases the hardship was brought on by not understanding that the soul is moving on, developing and searching for God. If a person truly has faith, truly understands that premise, the "hardship" of loss, of understanding the limited life on earth, would be erased. The pain would be gone if simple faith took root."

"It's so easy for you. You seem to know everything." I said.

"You too know and understand all. Listen to your soul. It has all the answers. Nourish it with prayer. Understand that the 'hardships' you experience are brought on by your fears, your sins, your doubts—your daily material concerns. Christ suffered pain, but knew true peace. His struggle as a human was to block out the darkness, the suffering, and remember that true peace lay in God and His will. In the Garden, Christ asked for the suffering to be taken away, yet He understood the plan. Christ flowed with the energy of love, never stopping the Way of God. Do as Christ did. He is the resurrection and the life. Live His example and you will see what resurrection truly is. It is leaving behind the doubts, the fears, the apprehensions of darkness, and moving toward life. A new life arises from this death."

I looked down at the blank chapter of Hardship, ashamed for complaining.

"Pray for yourselves and each other," he said somberly, "as the angels pray for you."

My eyes didn't leave the chapter.

"Within each of you resides the Spirit. You must learn to delve within yourself and remember the purpose of your journey. You are here for your soul. Deep within, your soul knows this and recognizes the beauty within each other, the Spirit within each other."

Without speaking he closed the book and beckoned to me. We walked back to the tiled corridor with its glass arcade of stores. I wanted to ask more of him, but it was apparent our session was over. As I stood in the hallway, he pointed toward another bookstore. Following his direction, I turned the doorknob. It did not move. The door was made of a heavy solid wood and seemed to be locked.

"Just ask the Lord," the Archangel said.

I stood still, not knowing exactly what he meant.

"Pray," he commanded.

I said a silent prayer and the door opened with barely a push of my fingertips. I turned back to the Archangel, but he was gone. Timidly I walked into the darkened store.

A small lantern illuminated the darkness. Holding this golden lamp was an Asian woman, dressed in a silken white kimono with Oriental embroidery along the sleeves and collar. She was slender and beautiful, her jet black hair pulled back into a large French braid which hung down her back. She nodded to me, her delicate hands still holding the light.

"Are you ready?" she asked.

"For what?" I replied, standing firmly near the doorway.

"To come with me and experience more."

I looked at her more closely. She moved slightly to the right and I noticed large transparent wings behind her. Her porcelain-like face smiled tenderly at me.

"You have arrived here. It is time to see more," she said, extending a small hand.

Holding up her lantern to guide me, she glided toward the back of the room. The dim light flickered slightly as we moved through aisles of books. Arriving at another door, I stumbled and grabbed onto a bookcase. The Asian Angel glanced back at me. "Walk into the unknown with faith. It is essential not to fear. It is essential to learn more. Come," she said gently.

She offered me her hand, which I gladly accepted. Her skin felt soft, like rose petals against my own. Her lamplight penetrated the darkness.

Pushing open another door, I squinted at the glaring sunshine of the outdoors. The heat was stifling. I shut my eyes. The smell of dead fish and the oppressive humidity overcame me.

"Look," I heard her say softly.

Cautiously I opened my eyes. We were standing on a dilapidated dock in the middle of a long narrow river. Small wooden boats with tattered sails moved passed us. Straw huts built on wooden stilts stood over the stagnant waters. The place reeked of garbage, sewage, and rotting fish. Poverty abounded.

"Come and see more," the Asian Angel said.

"Where are we?" I asked, already feeling the perspiration forming beneath my blouse. I opened my mouth wide, trying to breathe in fresh air, but snapped it shut when I noticed the insects swarming about us. This time I didn't take her hand. "I'm not sure I want to be here," I said.

"It is for you to see."

Within seconds we were in a hut. Obviously the people did not see us but we had full access to their actions and conversations. In the corner of this barren hut a woman was sitting surrounded by small, malnourished children. The woman was so thin that the bones from her neck, arms, and legs protruded from her body. Her tiny children had the same gaunt appearance. The woman's hair, cropped short, was gray.

"She is your age," the angel said.

"She looks at least twenty years older, if not more," I answered.

"She is dying."

I closed my eyes but could not escape the torrid heat or the wails from the woman. I could hear her small children crawling around the dirt floor. "Why did you bring me here?" I asked, still not wanting to see this scene. "I cannot help every poor person in the world. This is so sad." I brushed away a tear and opened my eyes.

"I brought you here to see how the body is controlling the spirit."

"What?"

"She thinks nothing of her spirit any longer, only her body. Her every thought is consumed with survival."

16

"I don't blame her," I said, surprised at my frankness.

"She is like many of you," the Asian Angel said, sitting down on a rattan stool, her eyes intent on the hungry children. "Poverty or riches, earthly things are consuming you, keeping you from experiencing your soul. Too many riches leave no time for nourishing your soul; too few, and your concerns are with survival. Many are consumed with achievement."

"Of course," I said. "Isn't that the way we were made?"

The Asian Angel did not answer my question. "Feel her hunger," she said.

Immediately I felt a sharp pang in my stomach. I bent over with pain. My body was so weak I could barely breathe. In the distance I heard the children crying but I could do nothing. Exhausted, I was ready to relinquish my body – it had brought me only pain.

Then the feeling was swept away.

Angrily I turned toward the Angel. "That woman is so tired, so sick, how can you blame her for concentrating only on her survival? She is dying!"

"I am not blaming her. It is her path. But it is also your path. She is just magnifying what many of you are experiencing on different levels. All of you are one and learning the lessons in different manners. But,"—she paused, almost dramatically—"you must learn to nourish the soul with prayer, or it will become as tired and worn as the body. You must learn to keep the soul healthy first. The body is only the shell for a short time. On this earth many are consumed with keeping the body nourished and forget about the soul. This is the lesson."

"*This* is the lesson?"

"Learn to nourish the soul. All of the concerns of this earth are fleeting and short. But the concerns of the soul are everlasting. Feed and care for the soul. Pray for each other. Pray that each of you turns toward the Light. Pray for the nourishment of each person's soul."

I sat down on a rattan stool.

"All of this is a lesson of faith. Faith nourishes the soul. It is important that faith take precedence in the world, faith and prayer. Do you want your souls to be ignored and fall ill?"

I wiped the perspiration from my forehead. "Of course not," I snapped.

"Such is the lesson. There are abundances for the body and they distract you from the soul. There is starvation and hunger, and that, too, distracts you from the soul. Learn to nourish the body in moderation, but concentrate on your soul. Do not channel your energy in the wrong direction. Everything is for love, to love and serve the Lord and be one with each other. You will experience every pain and joy that your neighbor experiences, because you are each other."

Barely pausing, she continued. "Always be kind to each other, for that is essential in nourishing the soul. Accept the gifts that God has given you. Open your eyes and see what surrounds you. "

I hated to repeat myself, but I wanted to say that it wasn't that easy for me.

"Listen to your soul. It is calling you. In this world of war and strife, jealousy and hunger, material excesses and poverty, the soul has been buried. All of the energy is dissipating toward survival of the body, which is a futile lesson. You must concentrate on survival of the soul."

I shook my head, unable to look the Asian Angel in the eye. "That woman was so malnourished that it is only human to be consumed with hunger. How can you say that people are to think of their soul when the pain is excruciating?" I waited for an answer, assuming I had to be right.

"Their pain can bring them closer to God and therefore nourish their soul. Or they can turn from God and try to nourish only their body. If that is the case the soul will still hunger, and that is tragic. The soul must be nourished." As she spoke her voice softened and deepened.

It still wasn't making sense to me. "When I experienced that hunger," I said, remembering vividly the weakness and sharp pain, "I didn't think of God or my soul. I thought of escape."

She rose from the stool and reached for my hand. "Come and see the way to God. And to each other."

Seconds later I found myself in a hospital. An elderly woman, her face creased with years of wrinkles, lay in a bed. Tubes and hookups were everywhere. Her face, although very old, was beautiful in its peace.

"She looks so sweet," I said, smiling at the woman.

"Her soul is nourished each day by contact with the Spirit. You are all one. You are capable of choosing either path." She stopped, and then added. "Experience her emotions."

With each breath I took, my bones ached and my ribcage felt as if it would explode. It seemed to take all my energy to breathe, yet I felt this elderly woman's calmness. My mind began to recognize the prayers she recited. Her prayers for her family and children were in sync with her breath, small and steady. Try as I could, I felt no fear.

The Asian Angel touched my shoulder. "What did you experience?" she asked.

"Calmness, peace, even though the pain was horrible."

She nodded. "She is nourishing her soul with the experience. Her faith has brought her closer to the light. Her love has helped her soul move closer to God. Her pain subsides as she breathes, prays and enters the Realm of the Spirit."

"The Realm of the Spirit?" I asked, unable to take my eyes from the sick woman.

"There resides peace and tranquility. Love can penetrate all the bodily pains and concerns. There the spirit takes precedence. Life is lived as it should be."

The angel returned with me to the glass corridor of bookstores, patting my hand slightly. "Learn that each of you is one, that all of you must face the Lord or happiness and peace will not occur. Heaven is on earth. Faith is essential. Everything you need for the nourishment of your soul is within your grasp and sight. Open your eyes and accept God's love. Turn toward Him and away from the darkness."

Before she left we traveled to other countries and met a variety of people. Of these places I remember little except that the messages were of a similar vein.

Later, as I typed, I wondered what I was learning.

The Archangel's voice spoke clearly: "You are learning what is essential for your path at this point. Absorb it, learn it, and most importantly, live it. Pray for each other. Pray for the nourishment of all souls. Amen."

Chapter Four

Fill Me with Your Breath

It was early January. My Christmas decorations remained up, reminding me constantly that the holidays were over. The red and green ribbons appeared anticlimactic. Postponing meditation and prayer, I decided to take down the tree and ornaments.

Yet the call to pray, like a subconscious urge, began again. Was I just feeling guilty for not praying? Regardless, I stopped, sat down, and closed my eyes.

Immediately I was in the glass arcade. The Asian Angel greeted me. "You are to write down the meditations and help others with them."

"What meditations?" I asked, peering behind her and noticing that all the bookstore doors were closed.

"Those which help people become closer to the Spirit. People are concerned with their survival, but these prayers will calm their body and nourish their soul. They are for the ill in body and spirit, who are many. They will help all."

We walked down the corridor, following the line of sunshine that beamed through the glass-domed ceiling. Not knowing where we were headed, I stayed close by the Asian Angel's side.

She touched a glass door at the far end of the corridor and we entered a beautiful small chapel. A narrow aisle divided three rows of wooden pews. The pews were painted a familiar white, but everything else was glass. The windows were stained glass in brilliant pastel colors. Flowers and crosses seemed the dominant motif. The altar was simple yet elegant, the table itself a thick bubbly glass.

"Face the unknown with faith and marvels will occur," the angel said.

"I don't mean to be difficult," I said slowly, "and I know that I always seem to belabor the same points—"

"You have progressed," she said, abruptly cutting off my remark.

Oh, I thought, had she been keeping track of my struggles, of me? I didn't respond, but listened.

"Prayer allows you to become closer to the Holy Spirit. People are concerned with their survival; these prayers will calm their body and nourish their souls. They are for the many who are ill in body and spirit. These prayers will help all."

I genuflected by the edge of the pew, slid in between the kneeler and the seat, and sat down.

"Kneel," she instructed me. "Give homage to God."

Quickly I knelt on the cushioned kneeler. But my mind was distracted; I needed to discuss something with the Asian Angel. "I have a friend who is terminally ill. She was fine one day but the next, her whole system just about shut down."

"Prayer will ease her path."

I shook my head. "She does pray. So do others. She's a good woman." I thought of her sunny disposition, her love for her family. "None of it seems fair."

The Asian Angel stood in the aisle, facing the altar as she answered me. "Have we not told you ample times that this is a spiritual journey? Perhaps this disease is bringing both her and those surrounding her closer to God, closer to the Spirit. And that is the purpose of life."

I remained kneeling, ashamed that I always questioned everything. I was beginning to feel a real affinity for the apostle Thomas. "Show me, let me feel the wounds, let me see everything," I often wanted to scream.

"Pray," the Asian Angel said softly, as if to cut off my thoughts. "Here is a prayer for the ill of body. Close your eyes and concentrate on the darkness that faces you. Breathe slowly and visualize the light flowing through your body. With each breath think of God. Let the breath of life come into your body. Ask the breath of the Holy Spirit to enter. Now pray these words: *Let my body and spirit be filled with the Spirit. Let it nourish my body and soul.* Concentrate on this energy moving through your body. Do not let it stop in fear. Let it move through your veins. Let it move through your blood. As you watch, remember it is nourishing both your body and your soul. Thank God for this opportunity to feed your soul and calm your body. Picture the breath of the Spirit as it is, powerful holy energy that can miraculously save and heal everyone. Such is the Holy Spirit. The Holy Spirit brings you knowledge of your life's purpose, and with this wisdom all healing is possible. Visualize this breath moving to where it is needed in the body. Thank it for being one with you, as all children of God are one with God and each other. Let its power breathe into the fear, into the doubts, into the disease. Pray. As you visualize this, keep thanking God and recognizing the power of the Spirit, the power of the Word, the power of love. The Spirit will flow through the body and soul. Remember you are all one. When one suffers, all suffer. Pray these words: *Holy Spirit, enter my body and soul. Heal me, and give me the knowledge to understand God's plan, that my journey is one of light and healing, and that you bring all of these gifts to me. Grant me the ability to accept this knowledge, accept the Word, and be free of anxiety. Fill me with your breath. Fill both my body and my soul."*

The words sounded so profound, so filled with kindness and wisdom, that I bit my lower lip to keep myself quiet. But I couldn't. "But what if my friend isn't healed?"

"It is the soul that needs the nourishment of the Spirit the most. The purpose of this life is for the soul to return to God. That is the true healing, the true journey. The Holy Spirit's powers are miraculous. The body is the temple of the soul. It can be whole with the spirit of the soul."

She turned toward me, taking my hand. A feeling of warmth and peace moved through my body. "Remember," she continued, "the Word is surrounding everyone. You must listen and love. Love is healing and kind. Bring yourself to God, and wisdom and love will fill you."

I kept my fingers wrapped around hers.

"All of you know this but have forgotten it. Turn toward God, breathe in the Spirit, and live as Christ did."

"It seems overwhelming."

"It is all so simple," she said slowly. "Pray the prayers, see the energy. Always believe and have faith, for the strength of faith is overwhelming. All things done in love are done for God."

She tugged lightly at my arm and I rose. We left the chapel and again entered the glass corridor. The bookstores lined each side of the hallway. The corridor seemed infinite. "The Realm of the Spirit," the angel said.

"Excuse me?"

"The Realm of the Spirit is understanding and seeing on the spiritual level. Prayer will allow this. Learn to devote time to the Lord, time to the growth of your prayer life, for the freeing of your souls. The soul cannot take precedence without your consent. Your body is a marvelous machine, moving and acting all without your conscious knowledge. Thank God for this miracle. As you begin to understand the physical and appreciate the body that houses your spirit, allow your mind to move toward the soul."

I stepped back, my shoes silent against the white tile. Shaking my head, I stared at her, as if to soak in her wisdom. "I can listen to this, write it down, and sometimes even live it. But, quite frankly," I said, "the minute something disturbing happens in my life, these messages become too difficult for me to act upon. I become consumed with day-to-day problems."

"Such is almost everyone's challenge," she said, urging me to continue down the pathway. "Nothing is difficult for the soul. It is perfect. Your faith will lead you toward this perfection and lead you back to God. Tell the people the importance of prayer."

"Tell them?" I stuttered. "Who am I to tell people how to pray?"

"They all know how to pray; that is not the task. They do not take the time to ask their soul. All of this is within each of you. But some need guidance in connecting with the Spirit. You must consent to the message. Turn toward the divinity. Realize that all the answers, even for questions you have not yet dreamt, are within your spirit. But the spirit must be unlocked and recognized. Communication with God allows all of this to occur."

I took a few slow steps, stopped, and then looked over my shoulder at her.

"Go," she said, "Go into the unknown and learn about your spirit. It is you. Yet you know nothing of it. You must learn more for this journey you have chosen."

"I didn't choose this journey," I said, standing firm.

"Go," she said, disregarding my remark. "Do not look back, but ask the Holy Spirit to help you contact your soul, nourish your spirit, and be one with the wisdom. Then the path in life becomes simple. Pray to understand all of this."

My feet felt like cement blocks. I didn't want to continue down the corridor without her by my side.

"Do not let the energy stop. Do not stop in fear. Go to God. Face and breathe in the Spirit."

My mind raced for excuses.

"It is the darkness trying to keep you from the life giver, the soul. Go," she insisted. "Pray."

Reluctantly I turned from her and slowly walked down the corridor. Ahead of me lay hundreds of bookstores. I prayed silently as my feet clicked against the floor. "Lord, help me to follow the right path."

"Pray," she called after me. Her voice faded in the distance. "Pray."

Chapter Five

We Are Not Alone on the Path

As I looked back on my visitations from the Archangel, the messages no longer had me questioning my sanity as they had when he had initially appeared a year ago. But I continued to worry and wonder why these messages had been given to me. After all, hadn't the Archangel initially told me to "write the messages down, and let them be known"? Those first compilations of messages had become the manuscript *Songs of the Soul.* In trying to market it, I had hired a New York literary agent and had even gotten so far as meeting four editors at one of the top publishing firms in the world, only to be told "the market is saturated with angels." Interestingly, here I had been thinking that my experience was unique and was afraid to share it with others, and now I discovered that "there were too many angels around."

Even that made me wonder. If the messages were supposed to be made known, why hadn't it happened quickly? I had done just about all I could: I had written a manuscript, shared it with people, and submitted it to publishers. My faith was shaken and I had become upset with God.

One morning as I settled down in the family room to pray. I closed my eyes to the harsh sleet that was beating again my large windowpanes. Within my mind I was immediately taken to the familiar beach. I searched for the Archangel but couldn't find him. As I climbed up on our rock, I breathed in the warm sea air. Clutching my knees to my chest, I waited for my friend, full of sadness. I cried out, "Why have you sent me on this journey, if nothing is to become of it?"

Immediately I heard the Archangel's voice, although I did not see him.

"Have you not changed?" he asked.

I clutched my knees harder, not answering aloud but nodding slightly. I knew what he meant. Before the rejection from the publishers I had wondered if the messages were authentic. Perhaps something was wrong—perhaps I had made them up. The thought terrified me, that messages might be published that were incorrect, which didn't help anyone's salvation. And I would be *responsible for an erroneous message*. At that time I had had trouble understanding the crux of the message: None will be saved until all are saved.

Yet since the publisher's rejection, since I had cried out to God, something deep within me had changed. On my knees, tears streaming down my face, I had asked again and again, "Why did you put me through this? I look like a nut, a fool. You're letting me jump off a dock with no water beneath me." Clenching my fist, I cried out, "If this is the way you treat those who are trying to do Your work, no wonder the earth's in such a mess."

No answer. Couldn't I have an answer, a sign?

In my despair I had reached for the Bible. It opened to Judges 6:11, where an angel comes to Gideon. In the passage Gideon argues with God. Gideon doubts, worries, and then tests the veracity of the angel. "Just one more sign," he protests to God.

The passage struck me like lightning.

During this difficult time I had asked others to pray for me. Prior to that I had never reached out to friends, never asked them for prayers. Amazingly, I had felt a new surge of faith.

"Haven't you sensed the difference in your progress?" the Archangel's voice asked, bringing me back to the present time.

"Yes," I replied, raising my face to the warm sun. I had sensed progress. Since reading Gideon that day, I no longer had doubts about the veracity of the messages. They were real. I had not imagined them.

"You needed time," he said. "And just as importantly, you needed to ask others to pray for you. By doing so and feeling those prayers take root within you, you understood more deeply that all are one. Without your brothers and sisters you cannot achieve true paradise. Before all of this occurred, you were sure that you alone were responsible for your salvation. Then you understood that you must pray for others. Now you truly understand your connection with others. Not only must you pray for them, but also they must pray for you. You need the others, as the others need you."

I looked around for him, but to no avail.

"Listen to the voice of the Helper," the Archangel said. "You need not see me to understand the messages of the Lord. Tell everyone this: Pray for each other and pray for the gift of faith."

"Faith?" The beach had gotten dark and stars were beginning to shine in the inky sky. I looked up, hoping to see the angel and grab this faith, like a star in the sky. Suddenly I felt a light touch on my hand.

My heart leapt as I clutched the Archangel's fingertips. "You have come back."

"Do not continue to search for the messengers, only the message. God is the message. Love is the message. Within Him is the comfort and love you truly seek."

I kept hold of his hand and began to cry. "It is all so much. I don't understand any of it." I stopped for a moment, "I don't understand your timetable."

He smiled. The smile was so comforting, so wonderful to see. His entire face beamed a radiant love. I curled my fingers around his, afraid he would again disappear. "My timetable?" he asked. "It is the Lord's. That is what you must understand. Do all that you are asked and the Lord will accomplish the rest. Your timetable is not His; my timetable is not His. His timetable is all knowing. Your path will turn and fork. As you travel, intent on doing God's will, your path will progress toward Him."

"I don't think..." I stumbled over the words.

"That He understands this timetable?" The Archangel moved

slightly away from me. In the dark night air his robes glistened, illuminated by a steady white glow. "Haven't you heard my words? He understands all. Your journey is as it is supposed to be. Do not be afraid. Do not worry. All that you do is with God's blessings. He is among and within all of you. Listen to the Word: listen to the songs within your soul. He calls to you each day, each moment, and each second. He always wants you with Him. Listen to the whispers of divinity. Do not block them out. Take heart in the comfort of His love. Such is the presence of the Lord."

I nodded, inching along the rock, reaching to keep my hand within his.

"Do not keep searching for me," the Archangel said. "You must accept the gift of faith; pray for it and take it. I am only the messenger, as are the others. We are only here to tell you of the Lord and of His plans for you."

"That's it," I said, bolting upright. "Tell me His plans." I insisted. "What am I supposed to do *now*?"

The Archangel knelt down on the sands. "Worship the Lord, listen to your soul, and pray for each other. Ask others to pray for you. The comfort you have recently received is from the Lord. He has listened to your beseeching and to the prayers of others for you. Isn't that a wonderful gift?"

I nodded.

He opened his staff and removed a brilliant diamond. "The gift of faith. The entire journey is based on turning toward the Lord, allowing Him to come into your life."

"Didn't you give me the gift of faith before?" I asked.

"No," he said somberly. "I asked you to pray for it. And now you are ready to accept it. Faith must be prayed for—others can help people on this journey. Once it is prayed for, the gift is accessible. It has always been accessible, but many need to pray fervently."

I slid down from the rock, feeling uncomfortable with the angel kneeling in the sand. I knelt next to him. "The more I learn, the more humble I feel. I feel as if I know nothing. The only thing I'm beginning to understand is that we are all connected."

The Archangel towered over me as we knelt in the cold grainy sand. "Community is the gift which you have been accepting and learning. The early church could not have survived without the community it begot. All of you need each other. You sense that you are one, but then forget. Community of church brings that to the forefront and you begin to remember the gifts of comfort, patience and grace. Each of you reminds the other of God's presence within you, and that the journey is so simple, so beautiful. Community is essential for the journey."

I didn't reply, but I understood some of his words. As each day passed I was beginning to realize that I was a part of everyone I met.

"And everyone will lead you to God, if you are willing," the Archangel replied, as if reading my mind.

"Everyone?"

"Everyone."

"Even the murderers and the criminals?"

"Can you not yet see?" he asked, raising his arms to the sky. "By praying for their souls, you will be brought closer to the divinity. Each person you meet, you meet for the nourishment of your soul. But many do not realize this. You move past these people with nary a thought. If only you were to stop and ponder their significance! You are there for each other's salvation."

I dug my knees deeper into the sand, trying to get comfortable with both the damp sand and the words. "Even the checkout girl at the supermarket?" I wondered if he meant more significant meetings, with people who had an impact on my life.

He nodded. "Smile, pray, give positive energy to even the chanciest meeting and that in turn will flower. The same goes for the negative. If you curse, you curse the world. It moves as the waves move, carrying the curse through eternity."

I remembered a time the Archangel had tossed a pebble into the water and I saw the rings of liquid expand outward, almost infinitely.

"Therefore, can you see the significance of even the smallest of acts?"

"I see it," I said, "when you point it out to me. But in day-to-day living...it's hard to think that smiling at the girl at the checkout counter has lasting impact on the world."

He stood up, an almost wistful look on his face. "Pray. You must listen to God."

"I know," I said, feeling smaller and more humble with each visit.

He began to rise from the ground, his wings moving gently, as if caressing the air around him. "Pray for each other and allow others to pray for you. This is the community of the early church living and breathing among you. Through this you will begin to understand the unity that is inescapable. Be one with your soul. Listen to it, write down the prayers that are asked of you and welcome the angels. But, foremost, listen to the songs of your soul, and the silence of the peace within. Meet and adore your God in humble love."

Standing up, I reached out and tried to grasp his hand, but he disappeared. I whispered to the star-filled sky, "Thank you for your visit."

Afterward, as I typed the conversations, the Voice became clear. "Community is essential for everyone's growth toward God. You are seeking God. Look within yourselves and look toward each other. Your souls are divine, children of God. Find Him within the community. As the early church thrived with such a community, so will be your journey. Within each of you resides the divinity. You must cherish and honor this divinity. You must begin to recognize the wholeness and holiness of your own soul and each other's. Thus you will begin to find the pathway to the Lord."

Some days the messages exhausted me. I wondered what all of this was supposed to mean. The messages came with such profundity and such urgency that I found it hard not to swallow them up, like nourishment necessary to survive. Yet as time passed my doubts and anxieties returned, and the everyday tasks of life took precedence. There were bills to pay, projects to be done, meals to cook...

Today, while I was drinking a cup of coffee, I turned on the news. The police were handcuffing a man who was accused of raping a nine-month-old boy.

How, Lord, can I pray for that man? I mentally screamed out to God.

With my help, the Voice answered

And I beseeched the Voice—whether it was God, Christ, the Holy Spirit, or whoever—help me pray for that man if I'm supposed to, because *I cannot do it alone.* As I continued to struggle, trying to erase the man's face from my mind, I began praying for him. It shocked me that prayers were coming *from* me for the criminal. I prayed that the man would see the evil he committed, that he would turn toward God and the light, and that he would understand his actions and ask forgiveness.

I knew I was not capable of praying for this man without divine help. That was clear to me and I thanked God for being a part of my life. I prayed that I could hold fast to His unconditional love.

Yet I knew I was not capable of that alone.

Chapter Six

This is True Faith. This is True Prayer

uring prayer the following day, I was taken to the crystal book store. Light streamed in from the glass roof. The Asian Angel stood beneath the doorway, waiting for me. Her white robes seemed to be illuminated in the plain room. She knelt and said, "I am here to teach you and the others to pray."

Immediately I dropped to my knees alongside her. Her long jet-black hair was pulled into a flowing braid. Clasping her small hands together, she said, "You must pray sweetly, like a child raising her arms to her mother. That is the way to pray to God. Innocently, with a faith that will move mountains."

Silently I wondered about her.

As if answering my thoughts, she replied, "I am neither male nor female, nor do I have a skin color or race." She looked intently at me as she continued, "Nor do you."

I must have looked surprised.

"You are spirit in a bodily shell. The body is nothing more than the shell. Your spirit is the breathing, living life force. Now," she said matter-of-factly, "let us return to prayer.

"When you are incapable of finding your own words to God due to desperation, depression or illness, you may want to pray this prayer. *"Lord,"* she began, *"Allow us to touch the divinity of Your spirit. Help us on this journey. Help us with our devotion to You, and to each other's journey. We are not alone on the path, no matter how lonely or difficult it may seem. We need only to look toward You, and our lives and purposes will be illuminated. Let us bathe in that illumination; let us inhale the breath of the Spirit, the knowledge of the Helper, the devotions of those ahead of us on this path. Let us see clearly the way of the Spirit, the way of the Lord. Help us on this daily road. Help us to pray for those who need it the most. Help us to pray for ourselves. And strengthen our faith, so that in this strength we will realize we are one in Your light. Amen."*

I swallowed hard.

"Pray," she said, making the sign of the cross. "Pray and love one another. Such is God's message, such is God's will."

She continued, "Remember to pray each day, and to hold tightly to the gifts which surround you. Prayer is the essential act of communication with the Lord. It is accessible to everyone, the richest and the poorest. God has given you this power. It is divine and unconditional. Even those who are in the greatest despair and darkness have such power available to them. Use it!" she said firmly, "and the world will change. Heaven will be on earth. All will be united in God's love and light.

"Remember these words. Heed them. Do not be afraid.

"Come," she said, rising and extending her hand.

In the small, almost barren bookstore I stood firmly with my arms crossed against my chest.

"Pray to accept the gift of faith. Prayer will allow you to accept it freely and to walk in faith."

Shaking my head, I said, "I want the faith you speak about, the faith that just accepts without questioning, but I must question. I keep thinking that my agenda makes more sense and if God would only see this..."

She smiled, something she did not often do. "God sees and hears all of your requests. He hears even the slightest of whispers. If you turn toward Him you will understand that the pathway on which you travel is headed back home, back to the Lord."

Hesitantly I gave her my hand. My protests seemed feeble even to me. Her skin was soft and smooth, without a wrinkle on it. "Come," she said again.

Within seconds we were outdoors with the torrid sun beating

down on us. Raising my hand to shield my face and eyes from its glare, I wondered where we were.

Large stone steps loomed in front of us. I trudged up them, barely able to keep pace with the angel's effortless movements. We arrived at a Buddhist temple. Its entire front was open to the outdoors, its roof elaborated carved. Walking in, we found a brown-robed monk chanting loudly. He sat in a lotus position, facing an altar that was covered with dozens of statues. Not releasing the Asian Angel's hand, I stared at the rows of golden Buddhas.

"Why..." I began.

But the Angel had raised her finger to her lips. Silently we stood listening to the melodic foreign words, the chanting moving rhythmically through the air. Staring at the monk's face, I realized we were invisible to him. The Asian Angel nodded to me and we stepped closer to him.

His eyes were closed in prayer. He looked as if he were in a trance. I marveled at his power of concentration. I had never been able to be completely lost in prayer, the way he appeared to be.

"Come," the Angel beckoned.

We were transported to a tiny dark room. Immediately I saw another monk dressed in brown robes. But this man looked European, not Buddhist. Silently he knelt in front of a crucifix. The room was simple: a cot with a single blanket, a dresser, and a small wooden chair. The dark walls were undecorated except for the cross.

This man too seemed transfixed in prayer.

I stood in awe, wondering how these men achieved such spiritual solitude. Studying him further, I felt the energy of his concentration and wished I were capable of such prayer.

Once again, the Asian Angel squeezed my hand.

We were in a child's bedroom. I sighed, feeling more at home here. In this darkened room a little girl was sitting up in bed, talking animatedly to an invisible figure. Soon I surmised the figure was God. In a tiny voice she said, "And help Mommy and Daddy." I strained to hear more, but could not.

"Her words are for her and God alone," the Asian Angel said as we watched her bounce her head and wave her hands excitedly. "But she is praying unselfishly for the others. Her faith is the strongest of the three. She does not have to pray for faith; she lives her faith daily. She fully understands that the God she learns about is with her at all times, just like the humans with whom she converses daily."

This is true faith, I thought. *This is true prayer.*

The Asian Angel looked intently at her, then back to me. "Tell the others it is important to teach the children about Christ, about Love, for they will accept faith eagerly. It will help them as they grow. It will help them in times of trouble. The faith that was a foundation in childhood will always remain. God will bestow blessings on the innocent of heart.

"Later," the Asian Angel continued, "as the child grows older, perhaps she too will have to pray for faith. But the cornerstone will always be there."

"The other people were praying for faith?" The monks had looked so immersed, so holy.

"And strength," the angel said as she dropped my hand and moved toward the child. I choked back tears as I saw the angel bend over the little girl and make the sign of the cross on her forehead. With barely a rustle, she kissed the child's cheek.

"Thank you," the little girl said out loud.

I didn't need to ask. I knew she had seen the Asian Angel.

The child snuggled beneath her blanket, drifting into a sound and blessed sleep.

Watching the sleeping child, I assumed our traveling was over. I expected to arrive back at the crystal bookstore or back in my own living room, but I didn't. We were again under a hot glaring sun. Looking down, I noticed I was barefoot. My toes peered out from beneath the hem of a gauzy cotton gown. I shifted my weight from one foot another, trying to avoid the scorching sands of the desert.

"Forget the matters of the body," the Asian Angel said, watching my foot movements. My feet were suddenly clothed in burlap.

The sands no longer burned them. Looking down, I wondered how the thin cloth stopped the heat, but I didn't ask.

We were on a high sand dune. Ahead of us stretched horizons of sand. In the distance I saw dark-skinned nomads wrapped in white robes settling in for the evening. Dusk was beginning to fall and the air had become colder.

The nomads formed a circle and began chanting prayers.

"They, too," the Angel said, "are praying for faith."

"Praying?" I shook my head and sat down on the warm sand, tucking my knees beneath my chin. "How can you pray *without* faith?"

"Faith is a gift which is delivered through prayer. It is always there for the individual, but to access it, you must pray. Do you understand?"

I wasn't sure.

"Pray," she said. "That is what we are telling the world. Prayer, as the Archangel told you, is the strongest power in the universe. It touches God deeply and helps you on your journey home to Him. Remember these words and let others know of them."

I felt the gritty sand in my mouth as I kept my eyes on the nomads.

She left me there, seemingly alone in the desert. The nomads' words became clearer, although I did not understand the prayers nor recognize the language. I only knew that the stars above me shined as I had never seen. The cold desert air touched my cheeks but did not chill me.

I heard the Voice. "Go. Return to yourself. Listen to His Word. And pray for faith and pray for each other. As Christ lived, so must you all. He is the Way, the Truth, and the Light. Live as he lived and the pathway home will be clear. Amen."

Chapter Seven

Without the Others I Am Not Fulfilled;
Without You, I Am Still Searching

The Asian Angel met me at an empty bookstore. The glass surrounding us warmed my body as I greeted her with apprehension. She seemed serious and intent.

"Community is essential for the soul's growth. Community is essential in the church, in the neighborhoods and in the family," she began. "You are not alone on this journey and everyone must realize that it is essential to reach out to each other in actions and prayer."

"Reach out to each other in prayer?"

"You have learned the power of others' praying for you, have you not?" she asked, tilting her head slightly. I felt like a small schoolchild afraid of not knowing the correct answer.

I nodded. As I was trying to find a publisher for the messages (and had come so close with a prestigious one), I had found myself asking other people to pray for the publication of the book and for me. Up until that time I rarely had asked others for prayers. It had amazed me how eagerly people agreed to pray for me. The astounding part was I had *felt* the comfort from their prayers. A new strength, power and conviction grew within me. Why was I always so amazed that prayers actually worked? I was usually willing to pray but always astounded when the prayers were answered! Whether or not I agreed with the answers, I always received the comfort I needed.

Why did I constantly forget that?

The Asian Angel interrupted my thoughts. "Community is one of the lessons that you are to learn. You realized from the Archangel that you are all one. Now you must take that realization another step and become one with each other through prayer, through forgiveness, through community. The soul is connected to itself and until each of you realizes this, it will struggle on its path."

From a corner I pulled over a wooden box and sat down. The Asian Angel, diminutive yet formidable, remained standing. "In the early church the community was essential. The apostles could not have survived alone, without the strength of each other. Christ set up the community and in doing so showed each person the importance of the others. He did not walk alone. He realized that the community is human and will often falter, but it is essential if His messages are to be learned."

I slouched slightly on the box, overwhelmed by her words. I wanted to point out the difficulties of a community when the United States alone had over 260 million people. But I was silent.

"Pray this prayer," she said softly. "*Lord, help me to reach out in prayer. Help me to pray for my brothers and sisters and their journeys. Help me to realize that without others, I am not fulfilled; without You I am still searching. Give me strength to accept the gifts that you readily give us, give me knowledge to accept their application, and give me peace to love my neighbor. Let me understand more fully the love that surrounds all of us and the light that shines on all of us. Let me pray for my neighbor, and in turn my path will be illuminated. Amen.*"

The idea that as I prayed for others *I* would be helped was an interesting one. Until these visits it had never crossed my mind.

Chapter Eight

Build on the Gifts

I found myself walking through the crystal arcade, without direction but seemingly with a purpose. The sun shone through the building's clear ceiling. As I looked outside, I saw a glass staircase that rose to the sky. Following my intuition, I opened a door and was relieved and delighted to see the Archangel. I always felt the most comfortable with him. I trusted his words and wisdom.

Within seconds he had taken me to a different location. We sat on a large rock overlooking a bustling city, which glittered against the dark night sky. I didn't recognize our location but I was sure it existed.

I settled onto the rock, feeling safe and secure.

"You have not been sitting in the presence of the Lord," the Archangel said.

"Oh," I answered, avoiding his eyes. "I've tried, but I have a hard time with that. The Lord doesn't come to me. My thoughts wander."

Feeling the Archangel's gaze, I looked up. His brilliant blue eyes penetrated me. "He is there for you. You must be patient and persistent. Pray every day, no matter how long or short the duration. Listen to the Christ within you. It will calm and protect you and bring you to the divine."

I nodded. He made it all sound so easy.

The Archangel swept his hand over the horizon. "What do you

see?"

I looked at the city.

"What do you *feel*?" he pursued.

As if a cloth were being draped over me, I felt enveloped in a tremendous blanket of loneliness. I couldn't explain why. I was with the Archangel and there were millions of people below us. Yet the emotion was overpowering.

"Lonely," I answered.

"Yes," he said. "You are listening with your soul. You are listening to the Word of the Helper."

So often he spoke of things that I didn't grasp. "Excuse me," I said, "but there are millions of people there. I shouldn't feel loneliness. It's not as if I were stranded in a desert."

"When in the desert, alone with yourself, you can more easily feel the presence of God. There are not obstructions. When you are with a true community, you can also feel the presence of God."

"Well," I pointed to the city, "here's a community. It's huge. How come I feel lonely?"

"Not all gatherings are communities. This is important for you to comprehend. When you are with a community, you are not lonely."

I frowned. This was beyond my understanding.

As always, the Archangel was patient. "Now tell the others. To truly move forth with this truth, you must accept the gifts and build on them with a community."

"A church?" I wondered aloud. I squinted, not having the best night vision, but making out a few steeples below us.

"There are churches which truly please God. Yet many churches are not communities."

"Look at all the neighborhoods," I said, trying not to be too argumentative. "There are tons of communities there."

He shook his head. "In many neighborhoods there are not communities. You must understand the workings of the early church. The disciples could not have preached the Word without each other. They are living examples of the need for each other, the need to recognize the One."

44

He continued without a pause. "Christ needed disciples to spread the Word. Alone it was not possible. That is the meaning of community. The disciples needed each other for support, for understanding, to help them on their journey."

"Oh," I said, "there are a lot of churches with communities."

He agreed, looking out on the city. "But not enough. And it is not only churches of which I speak. The message is not solely for those who worship the Lord. It is for all, for those who do not know how to reach God but need to be shown the path for their journey. Building a community will help them."

I still didn't understand. How could a community or neighborhood help people find God?

He smiled, keeping his gaze on the city. "When a community acts as one, doing good, whether it is to educate children, to be better people, or to help the sick and poor, God is there. As Christ said, 'When two or more of you gather, I am there.' Prayer comes in many forms. Helping each other, helping the sick, helping the children are all forms of prayer. The people need not know that they are religious or pious, or even that they are on this pathway to God, in order for them to be doing His work and entering the Realm of the Spirit. That will be shown them through the results of the community and the peace which ensues."

The angel turned toward me, his face seemingly illuminated in the moonlight. "Tell everyone to reach out to his brother and sister, to bring together the One in physical being. From this the spiritual will unite."

I didn't want to hear the "tell everyone" part. I sighed audibly. "Listen," I said softly, "I don't want to be argumentative, but I've tried to do what you've asked, to let it be known, and, quite frankly, it's not really getting anywhere. Editors at a top publishing house liked the book, but in the end the marketing department nixed it. It's out of my hands."

"It was not the time. Your faith needed to be stronger."

I shrugged. "It seemed like the time to me. How much closer could I get?"

45

"But is not your faith in the Word stronger? Is not your quest much clearer? You no longer doubt the messages, do you?"

"No," I admitted. That had been a worry of mine, but no longer. I had always been fearful of spreading incorrect doctrine.

"You are a child of the Lord, a worker to convey His messages," the angel said. "We know that you worried, that you cared and were concerned about leading people in the wrong direction."

"Of course."

"We have watched you pray fervently and struggle with this issue. You were not ready to share the Word."

"And now?"

"Almost," he said with a twinkle in his eye.

In the cool night air I saw his stigmata clearly. A bit of blood trickled from them. I looked down at my hands and saw my own stigmata, always amazed at my ability to see them in these visions. They reminded me of the sacrifice Christ made for us.

They seemed to be bleeding more than before.

"Sometimes the struggle is difficult," he said, "but I assure you, with each soul realizing its path toward God, the stigmata will fade. And when all are one in the Spirit, they will vanish."

Always appreciating his help, I thanked him. "I didn't expect to see you again," I said, my voice tinged with sadness.

"You have prayed long and hard and we have been sent to help you. God knows that this has been both a wonderful and trying time for you. He realizes that this period in the world is not easy. We are here to help you learn the necessity of the community. Now is the time to bring people together.

"Do not isolate one from the other. Remember what I have told you: Each person is in your path for growth. They are not there by accident."

That was difficult for me to grasp. "I meet a lot of people," I said, thinking of my brief wave to a tollbooth operator. "How can insignificant meetings have meaning?"

"They serve a purpose. You are to learn from the people, or they from you. You are to pray for each other. Pray for those who are your enemies; pray for the strangers. Then the community will become one with God and the soul. That is the way of the Lord."

The Archangel stood motionless, keeping watch over the city. Enjoying the brief silence, I tried to digest all he had told me. Dawn was beginning to break over the horizon and I expected to be brought back home. But the Archangel began speaking again.

"Christ said: 'I am the Way, the Truth and the Light.'"

"Yes," I said, recognizing that passage from the Bible, but I remembered the word as life, not light.

"The light of God is true life," the Archangel replied, answering my inner question. "Christ wanted people to understand the words. He not only is the Word, but He is the example of the Word."

"What do you mean?"

"Christ gave up His life for his neighbor. Do the same. He loved his enemies. Do the same. He took to the poor, the outcast, and the needy. Do the same."

I watched the pink line of dawn form over the city.

"Live as Christ lived," the Archangel continued. "By doing this you will be on the way to the Lord. You too will live the truth and face the light. He holds the lantern for your journey. Face it and the path will become illuminated and clear."

The words made sense, but applying them was always so difficult. "Sometimes," I said, "I feel like the road I'm on is rocky and under construction. Every time I get somewhere, there's a detour, or another bump in the road, or a roadblock."

"The Lord's road is never under construction," the Archangel replied. "It only seems that way to you. The way to the Lord is smooth. You need not follow the path of man, need not be stopped by roadblocks. When you see a detour, it is God's path moving and guiding you in the direction of the Spirit. Look at your life. See where it has taken you and understand the lessons you have been taught. There is never a road that does not have a purpose."

There is never a road that does not have a purpose. I mulled over those words, somehow taking comfort from them.

"Remember what we have told you: the pathway to God is simple. Only trust in His Way, give yourselves freely to His love, and be open to the gifts which are abundant."

I was getting overwhelmed. "Are we finished?" I asked.

He shook his head, his blond hair barely moving. "No," he said. "There is a prayer to write for the community. Listen to it, inscribe it and remember it." He took my hand, his skin warm and smooth like a rose petal that had fallen off a summer bush.

"Lord, help us to accept the gifts which surround us. Help us to reach out to each other and the community, for it is essential to understand that this journey is not a solitary one. As Christ sacrificed and loved us, let us do the same for each other. Amen."

I brushed away a tear at the sound of his voice, rich and deep, reciting the prayer. He always seemed so humble, so loving and so kind.

"Remember," the Archangel said, "the early church could not have survived without reaching out to each other. And this church, this pathway toward God, must have the same community, until all communities are one in love, until all reach out in goodness and light for their brothers and sisters. It is essential."

He paused, looking at me tenderly. "You cannot reach home, reach God, without each other. Tell them this, and they will find the divinity and support. And God will bless them on their journey."

Chapter Nine

Place All Your Cares with the Lord and Peace Will Ensue

The next day the Archangel and I continued our conversation overlooking the bustling city. As I sat on top of the rock, I complained about my calf muscle. Reaching downward, I rubbed my leg. The pain was excruciating. I was sure I had torn a muscle the night before.

The Archangel, dressed in a rich dark bronze robe almost chocolate in color, watched me rub my leg. "We have told you the fruitlessness of worry."

I was distracted by the pain and couldn't help but worry about my leg. "I hurt myself last night during Tae Kwon Do," I said, exasperated that *he didn't understand* the concerns that come with owning a human body.

"Yes," he nodded. "We saw that. Do you understand why?"

"Why?" I said, trying to stretch out my leg, a difficult task as it dangled from the large rock. "Sure. I was kicking on a tile floor, something I'm not used to doing. I think I gripped the floor too tightly with my toes, because I hurt the muscle that connects to the toe grip."

"Why were you gripping so hard?" he asked, but I had the feeling he already knew the answer.

"Because I usually work out on a carpet and I didn't feel comfortable on the tile. I was afraid I would slip on the slick surface."

He paused and said, "Please remember this lesson."

"Lesson?" I asked, aghast. "What kind of lesson is this? Don't work out on tile?" I added, "This doesn't have anything to do with spirituality; it just has to do with gripping the tile with my toes!"

He turned back to me, his eyes penetrating.

"I know the lesson," I said, miffed. "I should have worn sneakers."

He was quiet. We both watched a meteor fall from the sky.

"You were anxious and your body became rigid. You were experiencing something new and fear overcame you. By being anxious, you injured your body."

"All right," I said, still not understanding why this seemed of such concern to him.

"Such is the way of the spirit," he said. "When you do not flow into the river of God, when you are anxious and scared, you become injured. Your soul retreats within its shell and you block out the pleasures of the journey. Do not be afraid! When there is no fear, no anxiety, you move with grace, love and light through this journey. Your faith brings you along, never questioning, but always thankful for the opportunity to return home to the Lord."

I must have looked perplexed.

"The body can help the soul. The soul knows all the answers, but you in your bodies must open up the messages and allow the soul to follow the path of calmness and quiet. Forget your anxiety. *Just as anxiety brought you physical pain, so too will anxiety bring you spiritual pain.* Your fears will hinder your journey. Do not be fearful and your body will be strong. Do this also for your soul. Your soul will be free."

I watched him rise into the sky. His gaze never left the city below him, as if he were keeping watch over the people.

Later that morning as I transcribed our conversations, I wondered why I had such difficulty "flowing with the river." If there were a "lesson" here, it wasn't one I had elected. I would have picked more worldly issues—tax benefits or something—not necessarily spiritual issues. When I told this to a friend of mine, she laughed. "Your class was preempted. You've been put into a class that, whether you like it or not, you needed more."

Like it or not, I thought.

During some mornings (but not often enough) I tried to sit quietly and find the silence of the Lord. I struggled to block out the thoughts that kept popping into my mind. Yet stillness would evade me. I prayed, "Lord, I'm trying, aren't I? I want that silence and I want it now."

Even to myself, I sounded like an impertinent child.

Discouraged that I hadn't found silent peace, I had been making excuses and not praying. Yet, one day I tried again. My head ached and a quick, sharp and penetrating pain pierced the middle of my forehead. I tried harder, trying to find the silence of the Lord, and for a brief fleeting moment I felt a peace. But as quickly as it came, it disappeared.

Shifting on my couch, I tried to become more comfortable. But nothing helped me find the silence. Frustrated, I threw up my hands.

The Archangel appeared. We were at the rock overlooking the city. He tucked his arms and hands inside his robe. "You have been evolving for thousands of years, trying to reach the Lord. Why are you suddenly so impatient?" he asked.

"Thousands of years?" He had mentioned this to me before but I had dismissed it. After all, I didn't want to be that slow a study.

"Still your soul, place all your cares with the Lord, and peace will ensue. Remember these words and tell the other. *Place all your cares with the Lord and peace will ensue.* Wondrous and joyous events will occur when you turn to the Lord. The worries and anxieties that concern you will disappear with His light. Turn toward Him and listen to His Voice."

"I keep *trying*," I said emphatically. But even now, my thoughts were distracted by the hubbub below us. Lights were flashing in the city, and planes were landing. The city pulsated with life.

"Breathe in the spirit of the Lord," he said, removing his hand from inside his robe and resting it above my head.

I breathed, but the air didn't seem clean. Even at this vantage point it was city air. I inhaled again, concerned that I wasn't getting enough oxygen.

"Man has put up barricades to the Lord," the Archangel said. "He has forgotten the gifts of God, the many beauties which surround him. He has begun to worship his own work, forgetting that nothing is possible without God." He pointed toward the city. "The buildings, the cities, all are works of God, but man has taken credit. And in this manmade forest, he has forgotten to give thanks to the Lord. He has forgotten the community which surrounds him; he has forgotten all the purposes of life."

The city looked lovely to me, beautiful and sparkling. The stars overhead seemed to shimmer over the vast metropolis. "You aren't saying we're supposed to return to tents or something, are you?" I asked, hoping desperately for an answer I liked.

"No," he said with a slight smile. "But what we are saying is that the Lord is everywhere, with you and around you, but the individual has forgotten that fact in acquiring power. The thought of self-sufficiency is taking over and the return of individual power is taking precedence. I am here to tell you of community and to remind you that you are all one. What have been blessings from the Lord, mankind has used to block the Word. Remember that the Lord is all around, but do not forget the Source from which all this power comes. And remember, in the advances of the world, the true advancement is the growth of the soul. Please remember that all things are from God. They are for the One.

"Do not retreat," he continued. "Reach out to others. Remember the Source and the Helper, and allow the gifts of the Lord to give Him glory. Allow them to bring you closer to Him.

"Nothing is possible without the Lord. Trust in His care and breathe deeply of the Spirit. You will find Him in the silence of the soul, in the gifts which He pours over you, and in the presence of each other."

With my eyes riveted on the city I said, "It's not like it used to be years ago, when people had small neighborhoods. It's gotten a lot more difficult for people to reach out." I pointed to the huge landscape. "Look. There are probably a million people in that city."

The Archangel shook his head. The moon and the stars illuminated his face, washing it in a pale light. "The community is everywhere, as God is everywhere, and the One is everywhere. Reach out to each other in prayer, in community, and the people will find God."

His words confused me. "Sometimes you say 'look into yourself' and other times you say 'reach out to each other.' What am I supposed to do? You've got me terribly confused," I asked, running my fingers through my hair.

"Do you not understand?" he replied, as if he couldn't believe he hadn't reached me. "*When you look within yourself, you are looking within each other. When you look within the community, you are looking within yourselves.* The lesson is simple. Please heed it."

I sighed. He always had the answers and stressed their simplicity. But "heeding" them was difficult for me. I would try for a while, but then worry and anxiety would take over. Finally, I voiced one of my personal concerns. "I'm not getting the word out as you asked. And," I added, confessing everything, "I have to admit I thought you'd do your part to help this publishing process along a little."

"Has not your faith leaped ahead of you?" he asked, at last sitting down on the rock next to me. "Did you not find peace in the Word?"

I barely nodded.

"All of this is necessary for your advancement. The time of the Lord is His, not yours. Trust in His word. All things will occur for goodness. Pray and reach out. And most of all," he said, touching my shoulder lightly, "believe in the Word." He smiled, his face dazzling with radiance. "Rest with the Word and put aside your worries. Turn toward the Spirit and breathe in the Word. *His plans are magnificent for each of you.* Remember these words and record them."

I loved the richness of his voice; it sounded like heavy bells ringing from a church. Repeating the words in my mind, I was comforted. But I knew myself so well. After a few minutes, or a few hours, I would forget the words, forget the wonderful concept.

The Archangel stood up, extended his arms, and began to rise into the night stars. "When you are worried and fretful, remember these words: *His plans are magnificent for each of you.*"

"Thank you," I called out, surprised that my voice had no strength.

"And take faith, accept the gifts, and cherish each of them. They are as divine as you are." He continued speaking, but he was almost out of my sight. "And most of all, " he called, his voice clear and strong, "pray for each other."

I weakly waved good-bye.

Chapter Ten

Hear the Others

It was mid-January and the heating system in my house had broken down. Each year I vowed that the following year I would buy the maintenance plan which the oil company offered each fall. I had yet to buy it, and every year I always ended up spending just as much, if not more, for a few hours of labor and new parts.

As I waited for the repairman the temperature in the house continued to drop. In the cold I found it even more difficult to pray. Always looking for excuses, I headed for the computer, deciding that I would work rather than sit quietly and pray.

But as I sat the Archangel beckoned to me. Within seconds I was brought to a luxurious New York City apartment. Standing in the hallway, I admired the polished wooden floors and the oriental rugs. At the end of the corridor I discovered large windows that overlooked Central Park. I turned to the Archangel and smiled. "This is nice," I said, peering through the window and admiring the well-dressed people on the sidewalk below.

He didn't seem interested in my chitchat. "Listen," he said sadly, touching his finger to his lips.

I listened, but heard only the honking of traffic below us. I shrugged, "It's noisy. It's a city."

"Listen to your soul and you will hear the others."

"What?"

"Listen again," he instructed.

This time I closed my eyes and tried to do as he said. As I stood by the window, the sounds of the city faded into the distance. A soft sound began, and then became louder. I struggled to identify it. Then I realized it was a sob. A woman was crying.

I looked up at the Archangel. He nodded. "When you listen to your soul, you communicate with other souls. It is imperative that you take the time to listen. Each of you is essential for the other's journey."

I walked slowly toward the sobbing. It was coming from somewhere inside this penthouse. As I moved down the hall a part of me wanted to stop and admire the large oil paintings that hung from the walls. They looked like portraits of wealthy ancestors. I walked past the kitchen, toward the back of the apartment. With each step the sobbing became louder. I stopped outside a closed door.

"Enter with your mind," the Archangel said.

We crossed through easily. Looking back, I wonder about that, but at the time I just followed his instructions.

A woman whom I had never met lay on a bed covered with freshly starched embroidered white sheets. A clock on the night table read nine o'clock. It was apparent from the light outside that it was nine in the morning. The woman ran her fingers through her gray hair, which was streaked blonde. Although only a few fine lines of wrinkles framed her red eyes, she looked to be in her sixties.

"What's wrong?" I asked the Archangel.

"Listen," he said firmly. "You are not listening. You are one with everyone; remember the words we tell you. If you listen, you hear God. If you listen, you hear each other. Please," he said, his voice imploring, "listen to the souls of the world."

Nearby on her bed stand I noticed a bottle of scotch, half empty.

The woman continued to sob, her body heaving up and down. Cautiously I sat down on the edge of the bed, but my weight made no impact on the mattress. Sitting there I listened to her sobs. Without any verbal communication, I understood her.

"She's miserable," I said, stating the obvious. But what wasn't obvious was I *felt* her misery.

The Archangel stood, his hands folded beneath his robes. "Listen and feel this lesson. You must learn to communicate with others on a different level. Intuitively, you will understand each other. You know each other; you are each other. Over the ages you have blocked all of this out. In order to return home to the Lord, you must understand the trials of the others and have compassion."

"This money doesn't mean anything, does it?" I asked, though still admiring the beautiful furniture and the view of Central Park.

"Nothing," he said. He moved toward the window, his golden hair glistening in the daylight. "Remember that you can never achieve happiness with the material. There is always more to hoard, more to earn, more to count. And with this excess the soul is buried. You cannot nourish the soul when you nourish the greed within you. " He looked toward the woman. "She would give it all up for love."

I wondered about that statement. "Sure," I said, "but the minute she got love, she'd miss the money." He didn't really understand how we humans worked.

The Archangel stared intently at me. "The money is fleeting, the love is eternal. This pathway is long, but the time here is short. Those who concentrate on the worldly ignore the reason for the journey. God wants you to be comfortable, clothed and nourished. He wants you to enjoy the world, but this enjoyment cannot take precedence over the journey home. It is another lesson. With love, with the light, it is obtainable. The material is never enough. God's love and light are more than you can imagine. Small sparks of His love bring happiness. Being with the Spirit for eternity brings unmitigated peace, unimaginable joy."

He paused and turned his gaze back to the window. "Tell the others to look within themselves and listen to their souls. By listening to their souls and hearing the whispers, they will hear the other souls. Communicate with each other on this level and love will begin to flourish. You will feel the joy and pain of your sisters. You will learn their lessons quickly and they will learn yours."

"But how do you actually do this?" Things seemed so much

easier to accomplish when the Archangel was by my side. Alone, it always seemed impossible.

"Through prayer," he answered. "Prayer will bring you into contact with the Helper. He will bring you into contact with the Lord, with yourselves, and with each other. We have told you many times: it is simple. It is not difficult. Why do you constantly struggle?" His eyebrows furrowed. "Trust in the Lord and believe. Pray for the faith that will carry you. The Lord will enter your lives and the joy will be all-encompassing." He stopped speaking and beckoned to me.

"But what about her?" I asked, pointing to the woman. "How can I help her?" I felt drained, as if I too had been sobbing. Yet I didn't want to leave her.

"Now that you have felt her pain," the Archangel answered, "pray for her." He took my hand and helped me to my feet. My legs nearly buckled beneath me. "Enough for today," he said. "You cannot listen all the time. You become weary."

"Yes," I said, grasping his hand. I glanced back at the woman on the bed. She was hardly the type of person I would have prayed for: she was attractive, didn't appear ill, and had money. A photograph on the bed stand showed her with a handsome husband, children and grandchildren. I stared intently at her photograph. Her face seemed chiseled, either by plastic surgery or just an innate hardness. Yet she looked quite satisfied. Had I bumped into her on Fifth Avenue, I would have thought her life was rather perfect.

"Perfection lies only with the Spirit," the angel said, as if reading my thoughts. "With the Lord."

He held my hand tightly and returned me to my living room.

As I typed the conversation, the Voice spoke clearly to me. "Understand what you have been shown today. It is important for you. You often see other people and think their lives are easier and without worry. But you are mistaken." The Voice was even and strong. My fingers tapped the keys quickly. "Without the Lord guiding your life, without the realization that the Light is illuminating your path, your life is desolate, your soul is hungry. Remember not to covet what belongs to your neighbor. Only pray for your neighbor. Try to communicate with the soul through prayer. Remember that the worldly is fleeting, but there are many lessons for the spirit. Understand that true nourishment is nourishment of the soul. The only attainable happiness is in uniting with each other and the Light."

Again, as before, the words were spoken firmly: *"None is saved until all are saved. Heed this and listen to the whispers of the Lord."*

Chapter Eleven

This Is Not a Solitary Journey

As I adjusted a heating pad on my leg, frustrated that I couldn't exercise, I decided that I knew nothing about life. Nothing. Each time I moved forward, either spiritually or physically, I took a million steps backwards. I remembered what the Archangel had told me months before as I complained about my spiritual progress. He had stated that the pathway toward God was always moving forward, through the grace and love of God.

But today I felt as if the conveyor belt had broken down. I questioned everything again; the angels, the meditations, my sanity. Was I going crazy? But when I asked myself that, I knew that I wasn't. My life had changed drastically for the better since these experiences. I prayed more often, was less judgmental and had more compassion for my neighbors. Also, through word of mouth *Songs of the Soul* had been circulating among people and they were being moved by the messages.

Sighing, I settled down to pray. Soon I found myself in a strange place. Nothing surrounded me but light. Momentarily I was frightened. I stamped my foot and felt lightness, like feathers or a cloud, beneath me.

I didn't like it one bit.

The Archangel's voice penetrated the misty light. "Do not be afraid."

I stamped my foot again, fearful that this lightness could not support my body.

"You are always testing, always questioning," the Archangel continued. "You must move forward in faith. Accept the gifts that God has bestowed and move ahead. It is so simple."

Following his voice, I moved tentatively toward him. I grabbed his hand and held tightly to it. I felt much better holding on to something.

"You have much to learn," he continued, his yellow robe billowing behind him. "You have begun to see the universality of the One, but you have more lessons." I saw his face clearly, awash with light.

"Come," he said, tugging my hand.

My choices were simple: let go and feel groundless amid the clouds or go where the angel instructed. I folded my fingers over his.

The minute we arrived I looked around and loudly announced: "Take me back. I made the wrong choice. I should have stayed put."

The Archangel didn't acknowledge my statement. We were in the middle of a men's prison. Many men were housed in the same cells. The sounds reminded me of animals bellowing. Putting my hands to my ears, I tried to block out the screams, the music, and the blaring noise of anger. "Listen," the Archangel said.

"How can I *not* listen?" Even with my hands blocking my ears the sounds were driving me crazy.

"No," the Archangel said softly. "As I taught you. Listen with your soul."

I had no desire to 'listen with my soul'. These men were hardened criminals, most of them in prison because they deserved it. Looking around, I shook my head.

"Please," the Archangel said. "Please do as we ask. It is for your advancement."

I bit hard on my lower lip. Closing my eyes, I tried as I had before to block out the sounds, but it wasn't as easy. Deciding I would rather be in the Park Avenue apartment than this hellhole, I didn't give it my best effort.

"What do you hear?" the Archangel asked.

"Screaming."

"Go deeper. Connect with the souls. You recognize them from before. Each of you always recognizes the other. The pain they are experiencing is yours; the darkness they are enveloped in is yours. Listen to the songs of their souls; listen to the energy around them. And *look*. Open your eyes. You will see differently."

Tentatively, I opened my eyes. The Archangel was right. As my lids lifted, I saw each man differently. I saw a light beaming from his body. In some men the lights were flickering, and in others it was almost non-existent. Only a few lights were truly strong, truly visible, and those stood out like beacons on a foggy shore.

"What do you feel?" the Archangel asked.

"Sadness," I replied, surprised at my answer. "Total sadness."

The Archangel nodded. "The souls are trying to reach out to one another. They are blocked in darkness and they cry to each other for help. The souls are perfect and all-knowing, but mankind must listen to each other. You must free each other from the negativity which blocks these souls."

I was having difficulty figuring out what the Archangel meant, with the deafening sounds surrounding us. "Are you trying to say we can communicate with each other on this level?"

"Yes," he said matter-of-factly. "But the problem which arises is that many souls are covered—some more thickly than others—with shells of darkness, and their pleas are more difficult to hear. You must tune into this," he said, settling down on a nearby metal stool. "You must realize that the dimmer the light, the more prayers are needed to chisel away this armor."

I pulled up another stool for myself. Fatigue was beginning to get the best of me.

"Here is a community," he continued, his eyes gazing over the cells. "But it serves no purpose toward God. A few here are finding the pathway, but many are stalled, turning away from the Light. These men have no honor for themselves, no hope, and no concern for themselves or each other. You must pray for these people to build a community toward God."

My eyes were riveted to a particular man. He sat in his cell, bent over some object. As I peered closer, I saw he was holding a hardcover book. As I watched him, he ripped the cover off the book and began forming it into an oblong shape.

Into a knife.

I turned to the Archangel for help.

"They cannot hear God's whispers," he said. "They cannot hear their own souls crying out for escape. But you are a part of their community. Everyone must try to reach each other's souls. Look at one another and realize the perfection which is within each of you." He paused slightly. "This community, this knowledge, will clear the pathway to the Lord."

"I don't know," I answered hesitantly. By now the man had already sharpened the book cover into a lethal knife. Whom would he use it on? A cellmate? A guard? Himself? I had finally begun to understand that we are all one, yet I shook my head. "Communicating with these men," I said, sweeping my hand across the scene—"I can't do it."

"No," he agreed. "You alone cannot. But your soul, in its perfection, can. It can communicate with the soul of another. The language is simple: love. The premise is simple: One. The pathway is illuminated toward God.

I must have looked puzzled.

"Have you ever met someone and immediately you were drawn to them?"

"Sure," I answered, thinking of my husband.

"It is the souls connecting. They recognize each other. All souls have this ability. All souls can communicate. Prayer will help you achieve this." The Archangel bowed his head slightly. I wondered if he were praying.

After a moment he turned toward me. "Community is essential. Please let that be known. This is not a solitary journey."

As the Archangel spoke, I kept watch on the man with the cardboard knife. He had sharpened it to a deadly point. "I don't understand where all this is taking me," I said, my eyes locked on the man.

"See him?" the Archangel asked, following my gaze to the prisoner.

"Yes, of course." Turning toward the Archangel, I asked, "Is he going to hurt someone with that knife?"

With his hands again folded the Archangel said, "Not if prayer occurs. You can stop that from happening with prayer. You along with the others can put an end to the violence that rocks this world. All of you have the power to intercede. God's power exists."

The words didn't sink in. "I don't know."

"I have shown you the power of prayer," he continued. "Take this power and bring it into a community. And you will be astounded at the works which shall be performed."

I said a silent prayer for the man with the knife, but despite the Archangel's constant edicts, I wondered if it would do any good.

His voice strong and firm, the Archangel announced, "I will take you back. But remember this: Pray for the souls to break through. Pray for the evolution of the Word. Remember that all things are possible through God."

Within seconds I found myself back at the crystal bookstore. The Asian Angel greeted me before I had a chance to gather my thoughts.

She knelt and motioned for me to do the same. Quickly I dropped to my knees.

"Pray this prayer," she instructed. "*Lord,*" she said, her voice accentless, "*let us remember that we are each other, that the world is Yours and Your will be done. Let us realize that we are instruments for that goodness, we are instruments for that light. Help us to achieve goodness. Help us to save our neighbors. Help us to save ourselves. Let us be reminded that miracles are daily occurrences if only we step out in faith. Amen.*"

"Amen," I echoed, thanking her.

Amazingly, I remembered these conversations and prayers. As I typed this latest episode, I wondered what purpose all of this served.

The Voice returned. "You are trying to piece together the events in your life. You will learn from them. The woman on the ship was on your pathway for a reason."

My fingers froze over the keys. Instantly I knew what woman the voice was talking about. I had been trying to make sense of some events in my life, events that I had deemed "coincidences" and nothing more. I had recently met a woman who spoke mainly of her material possessions; she had homes all over the country and jetted around the world. Quite frankly I found myself a little envious, not of all the possessions but of the freedom from monetary worry and the comfort that brought.

In New York City weeks later, on the same evening I was interviewed by one of the largest publishing houses in the world for *Songs of the Soul*, I bumped into this woman in New York. She had flown in from across the country for a Christmas party. I thought the meeting was odd, but nothing more.

And now the Voice was telling me that this woman was sent to me for a reason.

"You must not covet her possessions. She does not have the happiness that comes with knowing the Lord. She was sent to remind you of the spiritual versus the material. Your work is the Lord's. Do as He asks and do not worry about the material. You will be cared for, we assure you. Step in faith; pray for that woman. She was not only sent to remind you of the spiritual, but you were sent to her. Her soul needs the prayers of others. Let her see the Light which has beckoned to her."

She needed my prayers? I thought.

"You are there for each other. Remember and heed these words." And then the Voice concluded. "This is the Voice of the Helper."

"Thank you," I said meekly

The words "*You will be cared for, we assure you*" echoed in my mind. I took comfort in them and hoped I wouldn't forget them when I needed them most.

Chapter Twelve

Selflessness

Sitting alone on the rock, I gazed down at the city. Night had arrived, and the lights of the buildings seemed to dance across the black horizon. Everything glowed and shimmered. I clutched my knees to my chest and wrapped my arms around my calves.

I felt a tap on my shoulder. The Archangel stood next to me. I noticed his bare feet on the rock. Tonight the stigmata on his feet seemed darker than before. Looking up at him, I wiped away a tear. "There was a terrible earthquake in Japan," I said. "People are trapped. People are dead. Why? What's the point of this?"

"You must realize," he said, settling down next to me, "that the pain is fleeting." He adjusted his robes; the hem of the dark brown cloth completely covered his bare feet.

"Fleeting?" I said, my voice rising. "They're dead. It's permanent."

"The body is dead. The soul is soaring."

I shrugged. "That doesn't bring much comfort to the people."

He stared at me, his blue eyes piercing me. "In these times of strife people come together. The body teaches the person lessons in unlocking the spirit and bringing it closer to God. The pain, which seems horrendous, allows this community to grow. People come together in times of strife."

Looking at the city below me, I found it difficult to imagine the earth opening up and swallowing the buildings. "Why don't we just come together in good times?" I asked.

The Archangel looked away. "It would be wonderful, but that is a lesson of the body. The experience allows you to learn what is valuable."

My thoughts flew from people trapped in earthquakes to my own life. I admitted, "I'm so selfish. I've said prayers for those people, but in the end, I'm still worried about my own small little problems." I couldn't look the Archangel in the eye. "How can I be so self-centered?"

He showed no surprise at my statement. "It is difficult for humanity to overcome the materialism of the world and concentrate on their brothers and sisters, on their spirits. Day-to-day concerns take precedence in many cases." He paused. "That is why each individual is learning lessons from this world. All of this is a teaching tool for returning home."

"How can I change?"

The Archangel tapped open his staff and a shimmering diamond illuminated the darkness around us. He handed it to me. The heat from the stone warmed my cold hands. "It is the stone of selflessness," he said. "It is always available."

I held it, but I didn't think it could be that easy.

"It is available through prayer," he said. "You must pray for the others. You must pray for the community. This is the lesson you are having difficulty grasping. *When you pray for others, your soul moves forward on its journey.* Each prayer helps not only the beneficiary, but also you. By praying you are helping the people in Japan and they are, in turn, helping you. Can you see and understand this?"

I wasn't sure.

"Pray for those in prisons," he continued, "and your soul, too, will become illuminated. There is a connection among all of you and prayer weaves this golden web. You are all one and all the energy of the world revolves around the community."

This creature didn't understand, I thought. "I have been praying," I said, "but I don't always get the peace and comfort you talk about."

"It is because you still have doubts. You have received peace and comfort."

"Yes, but they don't stay long," I interrupted.

"That is your own doing. You allow them to leave. You lose them through your doubts, your worries of the world and your concerns with the earthly."

I didn't reply.

"Remember the peace which God brings. Give everything to God," the Archangel said, lifting his hands to the heavens, "and peace will ensue. Remember these words and live by them. All concerns, all anxiety will be washed away as Christ's blood washed away your sins. Walking in faith allows a serenity to envelop your life."

It always seemed so easy when he spoke, yet so difficult when I attempted it.

The Archangel smiled slightly. "Do not *try*. Just live the messages. Pray, love your neighbor and value the community as one." He stood up, his robes rustling in the night breeze. "Remember that each prayer you say for another returns to you. When you are angry, pray for the perpetrator. The anger will melt away and both of you will be moved along on the journey. Each helps the other on the pathway to the Lord."

Chapter Thirteen

Strength

I tried, countless times, to sit in the presence of the Lord. Yet my mind always wandered; I was never able to truly still it. I prayed to be able to find the peace that constantly eluded me.

In this frame of mind I found myself on the rock overlooking the city. Again it was evening and the lights from below reflected in the sky. The Archangel appeared and without greeting me opened his staff. A large jagged diamond fell into his palm.

I watched the gem sparkle in the darkness. "It is the gift of strength," he said. "Please accept it. God is always present. Strength is always available."

I looked at it and gingerly reached for it.

"Tell the others," he continued, "that the strength which you feel eludes you is always available. It is God's strength. This is not your strength."

I held the large stone in my hands, wondering at the complexity of his words. "God's strength?" I questioned.

"You are not alone on this journey. We pray for you continuously. Each time you turn toward the light, turn toward God, we are delighted with your progress. Only ask and God will deliver His strength to each of you. You need not struggle with the weakness that buries your hopes. You need only to ask God for His strength."

I kept my eyes firmly on the Archangel's. "Everything you say always seems so simple. But it's not quite like that. I have taken these gifts of comfort, patience, grace and sometimes," I hesitated, feeling like an ungrateful child, "I don't feel that they're working." I hated the sound of my own voice; it was whiny.

His eyes did not leave mine. "You have taken the gifts, and that brings us great pleasure. Yet you have stored them away, forgotten them in times of strife. You know the peace of the Lord, but you do not always hold tightly to the gifts."

I slammed my fist against my other palm. "Why don't I?" I cried out. "Why can't I?"

He smiled, just barely. "It is a human condition. You begin to think that you know the pathway and turn, like independent children, to your own agenda. Listen to the divine within you; listen to God's pathway for you and the journey home will be a delight. Take heart in His strength. The Will of the divinity will move you homeward."

My voice was low, almost a whisper. "Strength?" I questioned sarcastically. "My friend received horrible news. The cancer that she thought had gone has now returned. How can she fight that? How can she just get this strength you talk about?" I turned away from him, not wanting to see any more.

The Archangel appeared in front of me. "Have we not told you before? Why do you make this so difficult? All of these gifts are available for each of you. You need only reach out and take them. This can be easily accomplished through prayer. The strength of the Lord will carry your friend. Nothing on this journey is impossible. Nothing is without joy."

My mouth dropped open. "Joy? She has CANCER!"

He took my hand. Together we looked toward the city. "This disease can bring her closer to the Word of God," he said. "She can find the strength of the divine within her during these dark hours. She can find the light which can illuminate her soul during this time." He paused, as if to catch his breath. "All of this is available to her; she need only ask and partake of the gifts. It is here the community can help her. Through their prayers, through their concerns for her, God will aid her on her journey."

I became quieter.

"Have I not told you before that this is a spiritual journey?" the Archangel continued, "an adventure of the spirit? The body is here to help the spirit break loose, help the spirit return home. The body has lessons that allow the spirit to break free. During times of sickness many lessons can be learned, many gifts can be accepted. The way back home becomes clearer. The fog which mists your minds lifts."

I could no longer hold my tongue. "It seems as if you give us the test first," I said, "then afterward give us the material to study."

He answered, "It is only because you have not listened to the lesson first. If you accept the gifts that surround you, the 'tests,' as you call them, would be simple tasks. The lessons would be joyous events. The Lord does not 'test' you; you are constantly questioning yourselves, questioning the Lord. The Lord is steady, comforting and waiting for you." He spoke the last sentence so quietly and lovingly that I looked downward, away from his eyes.

"Go to the Lord," the Archangel said. "Find the peace which eludes you. It is always there in the spirit of the divine. Listen to your souls, and soar."

As I was typing that day's session, I wondered for the umpteenth time if I were imagining these encounters. Some of my notes seemed repetitions from *Songs of the Soul.* And then I laughed out loud. Repetitions, I thought. The Archangel probably needed to hit me over the head a million times before I began to barely understand the messages. I had a new feeling for Saul, later called Paul, in the New Testament. I understood the need to be struck with lightning, blinded, before being able to see. Sometimes I felt that way, as if I were struck blind, and wondered if my vision would ever return. When it did, I was astounded at how everything took on a different appearance.

The Gospels too were beginning to take on a new meaning for me. I understood the people and their actions more clearly. We are all alike, today or two thousand years ago. We are the Doubting

Thomases and Sauls of the world, the Peters who denied Christ three times though he had sworn to never do such a thing. All of these men were people I could relate to, not for their saintliness but for their flaws. Their flaws were my flaws.

Interesting, I thought. Thousands of years had passed, but we were still so similar. We were one.

Lord, help us to realize that the World is one, that we are all Your children. We often seem lost and confused, but only because we have strayed from the pathway home. Help us to walk on the road and find joy in the travel. Amen.

Chapter Fourteen

Do Not Destroy the Gifts

The next day I was surprised to find myself transported to a farmland somewhere in the Midwest. The Archangel stood by my side while I surveyed the landscape. A silo was in the background and I inhaled the smell of freshly mown hay at dawn. In the distance I heard the sound of a tractor. A light morning mist covered the land.

"Why are we here?" I asked, inhaling the clean air and enjoying the new scenery.

The Archangel folded his arms beneath his robes, his posture erect as he stood watching over this land. "The earth is God's gift to humanity," he said. "Look, touch it, and breathe in this gift."

"It's lovely."

"You do not understand," the Archangel said, shaking his head. "It is a gift from God. It is one of the ways the body can help bring the soul back to the Lord, help unlock the soul from its prison. And you are not respecting it."

"*I'm* not respecting it?"

He nodded. "The world has taken this gift, abused it, and left it to rot. It is no longer helping release the soul. As you look at the beauty of nature, you can find God. But that beauty has been replaced with dirt, grime, pollution and noise."

"Oh," I said, nodding and finally understanding. "You're an environmentalist."

He laughed. "No. I believe in the purity of the gift. Would you take a gift from a loved one and desecrate it? That is what has happened with the Lord's gift. He gave humanity clean air, pure seas and beautiful creatures. The air is no longer breathable, the seas are filled with debris, and the creatures are choking on the pollution. This is what the world has done with God's gift."

The warm clear air around us seemed the antithesis of what we were discussing. "I'm so sorry," I said. "But I'm only one person. I do my best...I recycle..."

He shook his head in sadness. "This is the lesson I have been trying to teach you. The community is essential for the advancement of your soul. All are one. The community as a whole can change the course of the world with its prayers and actions. Alone," he said, "you are floundering. Together, you are invincible. The beauty of the earth brings you closer to the Lord. It is in this stillness that you can see His works, feel the Spirit, and understand the infiniteness of His love. But," the Archangel continued, barely pausing, "when this is blocked from your soul, it becomes difficult. The trophies of mankind tower over the beauty of the earth, clouding the sky with concrete and blocking out the stars. It becomes more difficult to be in the presence of the Lord and in the presence of His angels."

Following his train of thought, I began to understand why it was so difficult, almost impossible, to survive in the inner cities. The concrete slums hid the beauty of nature, God's gifts to His people. I felt a profound sadness creep over me.

The Archangel continued. "Community must realize that together this wonderful gift can be saved. Acting together can correct wrongs. This is for the greatest good." He turned toward me and smiled, as if reading my mind. "We are not asking you to halt technology or the building of your cities. We are asking you to think of the consequences before you do such things. Respect each other and respect this world. You are here, in these bodies and on this earth, to work your way toward God. His gifts are pathways toward home, but when you take these gifts and ruin them, the way home becomes more difficult. Nature is His gift. We are asking you, please do not abuse it."

Again I inhaled the fresh farm air.

"Many can find the peace of God when they sit by an ocean," the Archangel said, "rest by a meadow, walk in the forests. But these gifts of the earth will be destroyed if mankind continues its selfish ways." He stepped away from me, his robe touching the dewy grass as he moved. "The community must act together in prayer and then actions will result. Do not destroy what is essential for your roadway home. Do not destroy or ignore the gifts that God has given you. You must honor and respect each other and respect this earth. God has given you this present; please find within it the peace in which He resides. Do not block it out, do not destroy it, do not pollute it. "

From the expansive field in front of us the smell of newly cut hay filled the air. I watched the Archangel walk along the field as if he too were savoring the beauty of the land.

"We are saddened when we see the seas filled with debris. We are saddened when the cities have alerts for breathing. We are saddened," he said slowly, "when the animals are dying." He extended his arm to encompass the horizon. "This was God's gift to help you draw closer to the Power and the Spirit. And now in your darkness and selfishness you have turned from it and have lost it."

The Archangel looked away, his face stern in the sunlight. "Tell the community to pray for insight from the Helper, and then the rightful course will appear. The world is a gift. This journey is a gift. God in His infinite wisdom has given you these gifts. Enjoy them, respect them, and use them to work your way back home."

His closing words sounded like a prayer

"Amen," I said softly, watching him disappear into the clear blue sky.

Chapter Fifteen

Only Occurrences of Love Are From God

Slowly, I was beginning to understand the meaning of our meeting in different locations. When I was overlooking the city, as I was now, the conversation centered on community. I adjusted myself on the hard stone and wished that the Archangel had taken me to the beach, where we talked more about the individual's personal development. I longed to hear the ocean breaking in the distance and feel the salty breezes on my face. But today I was far from that.

Turning toward the Archangel, I said, "Something has been disturbing me. I was watching television last night, channel flipping, and it was late. Some evangelist was talking about the end of the world. Some of these people even give a date." I paused. A part of me wanted to ask him if that were true and another part didn't want to know the answer.

"Only God knows the hour and the day," the Archangel answered. "We can see many events which *may* occur, but with prayers events can change. That is the grace of God. That is the power of prayer."

"What do you mean?" I asked.

"See this?" he said, waving his hand toward the city below us. "In this place there are individuals who are filled with hate, who have the ability to build nuclear bombs. The knowledge of nuclear bombs and the ingredients are becoming more accessible. These people are concerned with their own agendas, concerned with the worldly. Some say they are doing it in the name of God, but God is not a hateful being. Only occurrences of love are from God."

Only occurrences of love are from God.

I looked down at my lap. "I can pray for them but that's not going to do that much," I said.

His voice almost bellowed. "Do you not understand? Prayer is more powerful than nuclear bombs; prayer is more powerful than Evil Incarnate. Prayer can change the world. Heaven can be on earth. The plans of men can be altered through prayers. The future can be altered through prayers. Nothing is impossible. The future will be a wonderful place if the prayers of mankind make it so."

My heart raced. I felt so dense. Hadn't he told me countless times that prayer was powerful?

"Collectively," he continued, "prayers have enormous power."

His opened his staff. A large glittering stone fell into his hand. It appeared iridescent in the night light. "This is compassion," he said. "Take it, and have compassion for those whom you have never met, those whom you don't realize exist. Pray for those who are on the path of darkness, the path of destruction."

"But I don't even know whom you're talking about," I stammered.

"Tell that to God," he said. "God knows all. Allow the prayers to filter through the earth and the heavens, allow the prayers to settle with those who need to know. Implore the Helper to pour forth spiritual wisdom onto the ignorant; implore the Helper to aid them in turning toward the Light. And such will be accomplished."

I tried to visualize prayers floating from earth to heaven and then back down again. It seemed rather comforting.

"Remember, you are all one," the Archangel continued. "If one can plan destruction, more can plan resurrection. The prayers of goodness far outweigh the desires of darkness. The power of collective prayer is beyond your grasp, but it is real. Always, God is bestowing grace. Take that grace and distribute it among yourselves through prayer. Even those in the most darkness, those who are the most ignorant of the Spirit, can be saved through prayer.

"It is all so simple," he said, his hand remaining on his staff. "All is simple with Christ."

My chest began pounding. I felt so small, so helpless. "How do I begin to tell people this?" As I thought of it, I started to laugh. "It's like that old joke: Why does the preacher yell at the people in the pews?"

He smiled. "The 'people in the pews,' those who have faced the light and understood the lessons of the Helper, need to share these. They need to move on. They need to pray and help the others."

A light fog seemed to float over the city. I rubbed my temples, suddenly tired.

"You must realize that this is a journey for your soul," the Archangel said. "Everything has been a gift from God and each person is on a mission for himself and *for each other.* Pray for those whom you do not know exist; pray for those who are in such darkness they do not realize that a light is shining. The Helper will bestow wisdom on them and such will be the true way of the Lord." He kept speaking, never running out of breath, never at a loss for words. Like water cascading down a brook, the words flowed smoothly from the Archangel's lips. "Christ's way is the Truth and the Light. Follow it. Implore God, beseech God for the ability to accept His gifts. Use these gifts. Do not store them in a place of honor, because they need to be utilized every day, every moment. Each of you must pray for the salvation of the others." Turning toward me, he touched my shoulder. "And the world will become Heaven, and the earth will radiate the light of the Lord. You will find your Way back home."

I touched his hand as it rested on my shoulder. "Before all of this started to happen to me," I said, my voice breaking, "I just went on my way. I didn't think of all these things. I worried only about my family, my friends and myself. Now," I slumped my shoulders, "there seems so much more to worry about."

"Do not worry," he said forcefully, as if shocked at my words. "Worry serves no purpose but to age the body and infirm the mind. Place all your cares in the hands of the Lord. Give your cares to Him and peace will ensue."

"I finally prayed that last night," I admitted to the Archangel. "I couldn't take control of these messages anymore, of getting them out to the public. I was doing the best I could and it was in His hands."

"We saw you pray to the Lord," he answered, "and that will make your pathway home simple. Pray, give your anxieties to the Lord. Then there will be no anxieties. He will wipe them away and carry you onward."

"Yes," I said. "I can't worry anymore about *Songs of the Soul.*"

"We understand," he said. "And that is the lesson you must learn."

I stopped cold, probably glaring at him. "That is the lesson?"

He looked so wise, towering over me in the moonlight. "Yes," he said humbly. "Remember the words you prayed, because you may change your mind. But the lesson is this: Do not be concerned with doing God's will. If you turn toward Him, ask Him to guide you, it will happen. Prayer will move the mountains you cannot see in the fog. Prayer will change your heart and you will be like little children running toward a loving mother."

I said nothing.

"Give it to the Lord and peace will ensue. His will be done."

Tears welled up in my eyes; the city became a blur of lights. Wiping away the salty drops, I wondered, why do I worry so much? Obviously my lesson was not to worry.

Lord, I prayed, let me continue to give You my cares and worries and help me to understand that if I'm doing Your will, it will be accomplished. Carry me along on this journey, help me to do the right things, and let me understand more each day.

As I transcribed that day's conversation with the Archangel, a sadness came over me, the sadness for always following my *own* agenda, not *God's*, a sadness for thinking that I knew better than He, a sadness for always questioning. Oh, Lord, I thought: Let me follow your path, not question it. Let me move toward the Light without worry, knowing that whatever You wish, I can accomplish.

Yet always that little voice in the back of my head says: Maybe I could do it this way? Or that way?

No, I tell it, turning off the computer. I will try to do it the Lord's way.

Chapter Sixteen

How Do I Get There, If I Don't Know Where I'm Going?

My right leg throbbed from my injury during Tae Kwon Do. Because I was favoring the leg, the muscles in my hip and back were beginning to overcompensate. Everything ached. Thinking back to the Archangel's words, I had a hard time simply "giving it to God" and not being concerned over earthly worries, especially about the acute pain that was shooting up my leg.

As I loaded my dishwasher, I focused only on my pain. I tried to block it out and pray small little prayers in sync with my breath, as the Asian Angel had shown me, but my torn muscle took control. Finally I gave in to it and sat down.

"I must be a horrible person," I said aloud to God. "You've sent me the answers, but I'm still stuck on all the questions." The occasional brief moment when I was willing to give my anxieties to God was only that—brief. Within days, or hours, or minutes, I was back to worrying about my daily needs, and what was to happen with these messages.

As I sat, adjusting my hip to accommodate the ache, I heard the Archangel's voice. "We are preparing you. Just as a meal takes time to cook, we are preparing you for your path. It will not be easy, but you have passed many obstacles. Fully understanding the will of God is difficult for you. It is difficult for you to not worry, even though it serves no purpose."

He certainly understood me.

"But when you fully comprehend that God's will shall be done, you will be able to demonstrate these messages with courage and confidence. You are being molded, being knit, all with your knowledge and permission since you have turned to God. Patience is a gift that you have difficulty holding onto. Grasp its warmth and feel the breath of the Spirit around you."

I inhaled, as if that alone could capture this breath.

"All of you are on a pathway," he continued. "You are being prepared for the work of God. Do not question this time; savor it. Savor the peace and tranquility. Savor the ability to listen to the messages, because soon you will be in the world and it will not be an easy pathway. But God will be on it. Thank God for the blessings He bestows. All are on pathways home."

Lord, I thought, help me to understand that if I pray for Your will to be done, it will be. Help me to understand that my vision is obstructed, but Yours is clear. Lead me, blind and unknowing, toward the Light so I can see You once again.

I got up, feeling slightly better, and continued cleaning the house.

Chapter Seventeen

Begin, and the Circle Will Begin

Each day I tried to sit in the presence of the Lord, searching for the peace of which the Archangel spoke. But my mind raced, consumed by thoughts. Trying to breathe slowly, I soon found myself on the rock overlooking the city.

It was dawn and a light mist covered the area. I did not remember ever seeing the city at sunrise.

The Archangel greeted me with a nod.

"What will we talk about today?" I asked, knowing that he always had certain topics in mind.

"Caring and compassion," he said, handing me a yellow diamond from his staff.

I was not surprised. It seemed like a lovely gift.

"You must care for your own soul. This is done through compassion for the others."

The sun was rising higher in the sky, making the diamond in my palm seem brighter. Fingering the stone, I mulled over the Archangel's words. "I don't understand," I said.

"I have told you before," he said. His robe was shimmering; it was an iridescent white with golden and silver threads woven into the silk. Continuing to speak, he kept his eyes focused on the city below. "Prayer for your enemies will remove the hatred from your own souls. Prayer for your enemies and for strangers will erase the anxiety in your own bodies. It will take away the toxicity that runs through your veins and muscles. And in turn, through this prayer for others, you and your bodies will be freed, replenished, and strengthened."

I rubbed my calf.

"Such is the way with compassion and caring. If you care for your neighbor, your soul will be nourished. This caring will return to you. In order to thrive and continue on its journey, your soul, like the body, must be nourished. Caring and compassion will do this. It is a form of love. Love feeds the soul. Love unlocks the soul from the hardened shells that have formed. This caring and compassion will feed your own souls, your own bodies, and you will find the answers within you. Self-esteem is within you; you will unlock the confidence that the Lord has given you as His children. You will discover the perfection of your souls." He turned to me. "Suddenly, like a candle lit in the darkness, you will see what God sees — the perfection of your souls. With this knowledge you will be able to perform His work. You will believe in God and the divine within you. And the world will become better; the world will change."

In the distance I heard a siren, and then another. I moved closer to the edge of the rock, trying to follow the flashing lights that were careening down a busy street. Even from this distance I recognized the blue lights of police cars. Crime was rampant, I thought. Didn't the Archangel understand this?

Perhaps he did.

"All of these messages center around community," he said, "and how essential it is to form a community."

More sirens. More blue lights.

"Love for your neighbor returns to you. Praying for your neighbor releases your soul from captivity. Without each other you would wither. Your soul would be trapped, blocking out the light and salvation."

I stared intently at him. Hadn't he heard those awful sirens? Didn't he know that some murder, robbery, or rape was probably occurring as he spoke?

He took my hand, held it tightly, and said, "*Pray for the others* and the prayers will return to you. Each act of compassion and caring returns to your soul, and thus you are freed. You find the divinity and begin to believe in the perfection of God's love. Your faith will grow mightily."

I looked down, again ashamed. Here he was telling me in no uncertain terms that he understood the evil that was occurring. Yet it was for me—for all of us—to pray.

"Remember the words, "*None can be saved until all are saved.* This is accomplished through and for each other. Pray for the others and the prayers will return to you. They will unlock your souls from their imprisonment. Your faith will grow in leaps and bounds and you will be able to face the Lord in joy."

He gently dropped my hand. "Go," he said, raising his hand. "Go, do the work of the Lord, and allow yourself to freely walk the pathway home. Follow the light homeward and you will find that peace which has always been there. You will find the comfort that eludes you. All of these are gifts from God. They are all accessible, but to truly implement them, you must do God's will. Love God, love your neighbor. It is such a simple request. And all of the works of the Christ will result from these commandments. Your soul will become free; you will find the messages of Christ simple."

Simple...

"Begin," he said, "and the circle will begin. The circle will widen and enlarge, and the example of Christ will grow within all of you. Such is the will of God." He paused. "Find your way back home through prayer, through compassion and caring for others."

The sirens had finally stopped. "Are you saying that all we have to do is pray and everything you speak of will occur?"

"Yes," he said firmly. "Prayer results in action. Faith will be given to you. You will discover the gifts that surround you. God gives these gifts freely. You need only open them, take them and live with them. But in order to fully use these gifts, you must continue to pray. Continue to ask for guidance from the Helper." The Archangel looked at me, smiling slightly. "The wisdom is there for you. You know the answers. The Helper will allow you to find the questions. He will give you wisdom."

I rubbed my calf again, feeling the pain shoot toward my hip.

"This is too much for me," I said slowly. I no longer really questioned his presence, but I felt overpowered by the messages. "I understand some of what you are saying, but..." my voice trailed off. Softly I added, "I don't want to be a religious fanatic."

"You are frightened of that?"

"Of course," I snapped back. "Who wouldn't be? I don't want to be labeled a nut, consumed with the spiritual."

He tilted his head, his expression wistful. "What other work is there? Have we not told you before, you are here to free your soul and bring it back home to God? There is no other agenda."

"I don't know..." I said, ashamed and angry with myself. His words were always so beautiful, spoken in his melodic yet strong voice. But my words were always questioning, always arguing. Yet I needed to be truthful with him.

"Your path is God's path. This work is important. Breathe in the Word of the Helper, transcribe these conversations, and the Word will guide others. Do not falter in your faith. The need for community is great. In prayer, in deed, in thought, the community is essential for your salvation."

I must have looked dubious.

"Do not question, do not doubt," he continued. "Only move in God's direction, on the pathway of your journey. Continue to pray for faith. Call to the angels; we are messengers of God's will. Listen to the whispers of the soul; listen to the whispers of God. These whispers are in thoughts of love, compassion and kindness."

Raising his hand slightly above his head, he began blessing me by making a sign of the cross. In the midst of the rolling fog, I watched intently as his hand moved from north to south, west to east. Encompassing the One.

I bowed my head in humility.

Chapter Eighteen

Only His Neighbor Will Be Able To Convince Him

The sun shimmered through the glass roof of the crystal arcade. In front of me, outside a closed bookstore, stood a black male angel. He wore a yellow and white robe over his stocky yet muscular figure. Without a greeting or smile he said, "You are now ready."

Despite my inner questions I said nothing. Walking toward the door, I noticed that the bookstore's window was filled with glass manuscripts. A few of the books were open and their translucent pages seemed to be almost golden in the glittering sunlight.

Together the Black Angel and I walked into the store, where he reached into the window case and removed a book. His hands appeared soft yet masculine as he opened the volume. Although he still had not smiled, his face was kind and gentle.

"Turn the leaves of the book. See the others," he instructed me.

The pages came alive with scenes of people in prisons, women and men of all ages and races, yelling and cursing at each other. I grimaced.

"Look deeper," the Black Angel said, turning the page.

This time the scene was even more horrific. The pages were filled with children of all sizes and shapes, most of whom were very young. Their faces were full of anger and hate. I saw none of the joy one associates with childhood. Many of them seemed almost unemotional; their expressions were of contempt. Not one of these youngsters was older than ten.

"Who are they?" I asked.

"These are the children of some prisoners," he said. "Look at what they have become without their parents' love."

"Hateful."

"They have learned the anger, which comes from hating themselves and their neighbors. This they have learned from their parents."

The Black Angel nodded, encouraging me to turn the page. I was only too glad to leave that scene.

Again the pages came alive with children. This time we saw an upper middle class school; all the children were in uniforms and looked affluent and well kept.

"Look closely," the Black Angel said.

My eyes roamed from the blackboard to the students' faces. I stepped back. All of them had the same expression of stoicism, a look of hatred and boredom. "Why?" I asked the angel. "These kids are well nourished, warmly dressed, and probably come from nice houses. Why do they seem to have the same hateful attitude as the children whose parents are in prison?"

"I will take you to their homes," the Black Angel answered.

I took his arm, feeling its strength beneath the silken robes. Immediately I found myself inside a lovely home. In an overstuffed chintz chair sat a slightly overweight man reading a newspaper. Around him were all the accoutrements of an expensive life: beautiful draperies, antique lamps, and oil paintings. Yet the house seemed cold. Everything seemed a little too perfect, as if a decorator had been paid to furnish the place. Looking around, I saw a photograph of the man with a woman and children, and suddenly recognized one of the children from the school.

"What do you see?" the Black Angel asked.

"Not much," I said truthfully. "A father reading."

"Look deeper," the Black Angel said. "We have taught you to look deeper."

I concentrated on the man. He brusquely turned the pages of the newspaper and scowled. Breathing slowly, I concentrated even harder. "He seems angry. And maybe," I hesitated, wondering why

I was going to add this, "a little empty."

The Black Angel said nothing.

"Why should he be angry?" I asked, pointing out the beautiful family picture. "What's he got to be angry about?"

"You do not yet fully understand," the Black Angel said softly. "Without God in your lives, there is no true happiness. This man can search forever for money, power, strength, but none of this will bring him peace and contentment. And this too is a prison. Because of this he too gives his children anger and discontentment.

I wasn't sure about that.

"There are many prisons, but freedom of the soul comes only with a commitment to the way of God, only in turning toward the Light. This must occur through prayer and acceptance of the gifts. If this man turns toward the spiritual level and channels his energies toward that, his scowl will melt away. He will find the peace and true success which escapes him now."

"I don't know," I said, shaking my head. "This man looks successful to me. If we asked him, I bet he'd say he was happy." I faced the Black Angel. "He's successful, thinks he's right, and is content. It looks like he has a pretty wife and kids. No one looks sick. I know people like this man. I don't think you could convince him that he's in some sort of prison."

The Black Angel stared directly into my eyes. "Only his neighbor will be able to convince him."

"What do you mean?"

"Pray for him and God will enter his life. He will realize that during this time his soul was locked in a prison, similar to the prison you viewed earlier."

I mulled it over.

"He will understand that the years were not filled with joy or success. True joy and success can be found only through God. Pray for this man, and when he finds this peace, he in turn will teach his children. Such is the Circle of Christ."

"Oh," I said, unable to absorb it all. "May I leave now? I've seen enough for today."

He smiled, his face awash in a bright light. "You have seen and recorded much, but it is all for the community and the blessings of the Lord. This is truly a gift."

I became quiet. Here I was, always arguing, always doubting, and the angel said that this was truly a gift. What kind of person was I?

Once back in the crystal arcade, the Black Angel instructed me to kneel and pray. "Open the doors of your mind and view the Lord in all His Splendor," he said, bowing his head and blessing me.

I prayed until I was returned to my living room.

Chapter Nineteen

Collective Prayer

The following day a different angel greeted me in the crystal arcade. Her looks surprised me. She was dark-skinned and wore a pink turban; her wings were white with thin strands of silver running through them. Looking around, I tried to find the Archangel, my familiar friend, but he was nowhere in sight.

"Who are you?" I finally asked. Even as I voiced my question I was certain she was Middle Eastern.

"I am here to tell you of collective prayer," she answered.

"I know all about that," I said impatiently. "People do that all the time in church. Pray collectively."

"Yes," she said, folding her slender hands together in prayer. "But collective prayer is an important vehicle of prayer. It brings the community together. Christ asked the disciples to stay with Him in the garden and pray. He realized the importance of the prayer of the community, how it brings the energy of love to one another. The prayers become more powerful."

She unfolded her hands, extending one to me. "Please come with me," she said gently.

I stood firmly. "I've seen a lot recently," I faltered, "and I feel, well, overloaded."

"It is your choice," she said, her arm still reaching out to me. "It is your path, but you are ready."

Against my better judgment, I took her hand.

She transported me to the Middle East. People were congregating, carrying small prayer rugs beneath their arms. Music haunted the air, summoning them to a mosque. I assumed it was a call to Mecca, though I was not sure.

"They are praying collectively," the Turbaned Angel said.

"But not to Christ," I replied.

"When they follow the Way, the Truth, and the Light, loving God and loving their neighbor, they are living Christ's example. The lesson here is the power of collective prayer, the power of community. Feel the energy."

I shook my head. "I don't know about this..."

"If in your heart you follow the Way, the Truth, and the Light, you are redeeming your nature and the nature of your neighbor. You are moving toward God on the path."

"Please," I implored, "please bring me home. This is too foreign to me, too different. I'm not sure that this is right. You give me Christian messages, then bring me to a Muslim country." I stopped, catching my breath. "I don't understand."

"You will," she said, her eyes alight with wonderment. "Today the lesson is to pray collectively. The power becomes intensified."

Chapter Twenty

Hope

Some days I had faith and other days I lost it. My husband had had trouble with his retina, and we returned to Boston Eye and Ear for a second evaluation four months after the first. This time the news was good. His eye wasn't perfectly healthy, but to the apparent surprise of the doctor, the condition had not only stabilized but improved. Sighing in relief, I thanked God, and I thanked the Archangel for his intercession to God.

During that uncertain period my faith in prayers, regardless of the outcome, had grown. Yet only a few days later I resumed questioning God on small mundane matters.

The Archangel appeared to me, standing at the far end of the beach. We hadn't met there in a long time.

"You are floundering," he said. "But your prayers keep you in touch with the Spirit. When the doubts and apprehensions of the world try to separate you from the Lord, keep in contact with the divine, with the Helper. The wisdom which is necessary will pour forth onto you like rays of sunshine after the darkness."

"It's so nice to be back here," I said, letting the warm breeze touch my cheeks. "I feel so comfortable here, more so than when we overlooked the city." I fingered the robe that covered my body. It was a beautiful yellow silk, smooth to the touch. I breathed in the salt air.

"Here," the Archangel said, "is where you realized that all are one."

I nodded.

"The city is to teach you lessons of the community. You are to learn that the community is essential for the rebirth of the soul, for the unlocking of the divine within you."

Tucking my knees close to my chest, I looked out toward the ocean. We sat in a comfortable silence for a few minutes, and then I broke it. "I'm having trouble praying for others," I said, my voice barely audible. "It's not that I doubt I should, but it seems that my own problems take precedence."

"We understand," he said, without judgment in his voice.

Above us a small group of angels floated past, and the Archangel smiled at them. I watched intently as they flew softly and silently overhead. "What are they doing?" I asked.

"Encouraging the world to pray. With soft whispers they delight in being messengers of God. Let it be known that they are present for everyone; people need only to ask."

The angels disappeared into the clouds, and we sat silently listening to the small waves breaking on the sands. I wrapped my arms around my knees, as if doing that would contain the question I needed to ask. Finally I addressed the Archangel. "Here's the trouble I have," I said, trying not to sound disrespectful. "Sometimes I pray a lot, and I know I ask a lot of the Lord, but often I don't get answers."

"You are always receiving answers." He waved his arm as if to encompass the waters. "Look around you. The answers are there. Perhaps it is not the answers you wished for, and therefore you feel abandoned, but God is always present, always listening. In your darkest hours the Spirit surrounds you when you call for help. The soul needs to soar and God is constantly beckoning it. If you listen, truly listen, God is answering your prayers. When you ask with a pure heart, the answers will be easily seen."

I shook my head. "No," I said. "I ask with a pure heart, and I don't think I see any answers."

"Yes, you do," he said firmly.

My arms dropped to my sides. "Maybe I do," I stuttered, unsure if I could win this argument. "I'm just not ready for the answers, or don't agree with them." I paused. "Let's talk about something else."

"Yes," he said. "It is time to speak of hope."

The Archangel reached into his staff, opened it, and a multitude of diamonds cascaded onto the sands. "Take it," he said, pointing to a large pink diamond, "and hold it to your heart. Hope is a gift from God. Hope leads you to prayer, to faith, to the divine. Nothing can be accomplished without hope. Without hope there is despair, despair of never reuniting with God. Despair is evil, and this negativity grows at astounding rates. It consumes the body and eventually the soul. Depression and anger result without hope." He shook his head sadly. "Such is a terrible state."

I reached for the glittering stone, knowing that I needed it desperately. I grasped it, rubbing my fingers around the sharp edges. It felt warm as I held it.

"Reach out," the Archangel continued, "and take the hope which God offers. Christ's message is one of hope and optimism: to be reunited with God, to make the journey home. Christ relied on the community to spread the message to one another. The need for community is as strong now as it was during that period. Everyone must become a disciple to each other; all are lambs flocking toward the Lord. As Christ went looking for the wayward lamb, so must all of you. All of the lambs must be returned to the flock. This is the essential message. All must care for the others. This is a message of hope and light."

Trying to let his words sink in, I closed my eyes. A warm ocean breeze touched my cheeks, and in the background I heard both the water and the rustling of the Archangel's massive wings. Opening my eyes, I was ready to continue our conversation. To my astonishment, the Archangel had transported me to the rock overlooking the city.

Pointing to the sprawling metropolis, he said, "Here there are many lambs, some wandering from the fold. Each of you, with the hope and direction that is from the Lord, must find the others and return them to the fold. That was Christ's message for the community then. It is His message today." The Archangel stopped, looked at me intently, and said, "Go and preach this word. Transcribe it, and live it."

I grasped the pink diamond even more tightly. I prayed I would not drop it after the Archangel left me, or lose it as I so often lost the gifts.

The Archangel left, leaving me alone on the rock overlooking the city. The sun began to rise behind the skyscrapers, and the sounds and sights of the city reverberated in my senses - honking cars and trucks, sirens, the smell of polluted air.

Lord, I prayed silently, help me on this journey. Help me.

The Voice answered me. "Remember the parable of the Prodigal Son. This will remind you of the messages. Take this story and live it. Let the community understand its power. These are the stories that live on forever. The prodigal son is your brother or sister in the prisons, in the streets, stealing and murdering. Find the prodigal sons and daughters of Christ, reach out to them like lost lambs, and bring them back to the fold with the loving arms of a mother. That is the message of salvation. That is the message that Christ lived and taught. Reread the lessons and live them. Do not envy the prodigal daughter for being blessed without earning it. All of you are blessed through the Spirit, but you need the prodigal daughter as much as she needs you. You are saved through the prayers and love you give to her. And she is saved through your prayers. It is a circle of disciples, working with each other, praying for each other, bringing each other closer together and returning home."

In my mind I play back the words: *Do not envy the prodigal daughter for being blessed without earning it.* This Voice knew my objections all too well, and put me in my place even more quickly by saying that all of us had been blessed.

In church the previous Sunday the sermon had centered on a passage from Corinthians that spoke about the body being one. It seemed as if everywhere I turned messages of unity were being shown to me. I must go to the Bible and find that passage, I thought.

Could it be that Paul understood this oneness? Could it be oneness was truly Christ's message?

I turned off the computer. I was too tired to write any more.

Later that afternoon I thought back to the messages that had been given to me. I sat at the computer, trying to go back to writing a novel about suspense and revenge. It had all seemed so entertaining prior to these messages, and now...well, now it seemed rather empty in comparison to the writing I was doing each morning after prayer.

With my fingers poised above the keys, I wondered. What good was transcribing the messages and conversations if I wasn't getting a publisher for them?

To my surprise, the Voice answered my whining. "Walk in Faith. We are preparing you."

For what? I thought. Writing down the messages and circulating them to a limited audience of friends didn't seem like enough.

"What is more important than the Word of the Lord?" the Voice continued.

Nothing, I answered silently. Not when it's put that way.

"Do as you have been asked. Do not doubt. And continue to write these words. The Helper will give you wisdom; the Spirit will work within you. And Christ will walk beside you. Each will help lead you home. No longer question anything. That is what we are to tell you. You are doing the Lord's work; that is the most important. Continue doing this and the Word will be made known."

I swallowed hard. "I know you have a timetable, or at least I assume you do. Do you think you could speed it up? I'm getting a little discouraged."

"When the Word is ready, it will be spoken. The world needs encouragement and these words bring it to them. The angels are working hard. Please pray for them to deliver the word."

"*Pray for them?*" I asked.

"God sends them additional strength."

I rested my fingers on the keyboard. "Prayer really is the key here, isn't it?"

"Yes," the Voice said. "With prayer comes wisdom and faith. And the Lord awaits you. Tell the community to walk in faith, in hope and in caring. All can be accomplished if you follow the words of Christ, the way of Christ. Is it not simple?"

I sighed. Hardly, I wanted to say, but that sounded so disrespectful.

Chapter Twenty-One

Believe in This

My faith seemed to be slowly growing stronger. Perhaps I was finally holding more tightly to the gift of hope. I handed more to God during my periods of doubt and anguish. "Take this. You carry it," I'd say, and somehow the burden became lighter. Knowing myself well, I realized I wouldn't give up control forever, but those times that I did brought me a sense of peace.

One day after I finished transcribing but before I turned off the computer, the Voice said loudly, "*If you only knew God's plans for each of you, you would not be anxious. Believe in this and walk in faith.*"

The following day the Archangel appeared on the rock overlooking the beach. A flock of seagulls floated serenely behind the crashing waves. The Archangel's light blue robe, almost the color of the sky, shimmered in the bright sunlight. Thick golden threads of silk bordered the hems of the sleeves and the robe.

"Hope is essential," he said quietly, also watching the birds. "Just as crying and depression change the chemicals in your body, so do hope and optimism. Everything and everyone are connected. Others feel the power you generate. The feelings you harbor make their way through your mind and body and penetrate your soul. Negativity and helplessness build the shell thicker, poison the body and pollute the world. All of this can occur through one person. Think of the magnitude when this negativity is multiplied throughout the earth."

It was beyond my grasp.

He sat next to me, still towering over me. "Again," he said, "we return to the community. The power of good in the community can outweigh the power of negativity. But it must be released, taught and implemented. Prayer will allow miracles to happen. When a community turns toward God, faith and optimism will follow."

My eyes were no longer on the sea. I listened intently to the rich, flawless voice of the Archangel. Each word was said purposefully and kindly. His tone, never condescending or harsh, was always filled with unending patience. "Today," he continued, "in your world, the people are striving for communities and families. For these groups to thrive, the people must turn toward the light. When they do, the communities will be blessed, their work will be blessed, and the people will be blessed. This will occur through prayer." He looked me squarely in the eye. "Prayer will result in actions and the return of the spirit to the light." He stopped, and then added, "Remember these words and heed them."

Prayer will result in actions, I repeated in my mind.

He made the sign of the cross in the air above me and rose into the sky.

I took a deep breath and noticed I was no longer at the beach, but was overlooking the bustling city.

When did that happen? Was I blind to everything?

Each Sunday our Church conducted different "adult education" programs, a type of Sunday school for grownups. While the teacher who usually conducted the class was on sabbatical, several parishioners and guest speakers were to fill in for six weeks. I was slated to speak about my experiences on the third week. I could feel my head pounding at the thought of telling sixty people about my experience with an angel.

Friends of mine gave the first lecture. Afterward I stood with a small group, eager to congratulate them. As I waited a woman in her seventies approached me. We began talking, and I voiced my concerns about my upcoming lecture.

"What's your topic?" she asked.

"Angels," I answered, thinking that was enough to tell her.

"Oh," she said, her face lighting up. "I believe in angels."

"Good," I answered, half-flippantly. "Make sure you come to my talk. I can use all the help I can get. I don't even know where to start."

"Start with the Bible," she said eagerly. "I'll show you. Come with me." She tugged on my arm.

I followed her up the stairs of the church into the computer room. "Here," she said, quite professionally, pointing toward a chair. "Sit."

I did.

"I'll show you everywhere an angel exists in the Bible. Pick out what you need, and the lecture will go perfectly."

Within seconds the computer was humming. She began to explain that she did volunteer work at the church. "You don't think the Reverends know all those Bible passages, do you?" she said with a wink.

There on the screen each passage with the word "angel" began to scroll up. The word angel appeared 207 times in 195 verses of the Old and New Testaments.

My mouth dropped open. This was just what I needed, something of substance to begin my lecture before I jumped into my own story. She said, "Give me a topic for the angels."

"Dreams," I said, thinking my experience was similar to a daydream.

She printed out many.

"Crisis," I spouted.

Again she printed.

"Fearing the apparition of angels. Saving people in emergencies. Bringing comfort and faith." I was on a roll. Of course I added, "Doubting the existence of angels."

She printed out Gideon, but I was more than familiar with that passage.

I thanked her profusely, already forming the introduction of my lecture. "I can't believe this happened," I said to her, flipping through the printed sheets. "It's just what I needed."

She looked directly at me, brushing a strand of gray hair from her face. "Oh, it wasn't a coincidence. No," she said, turning off her computer. "Things like this are never coincidences."

I was beginning to believe she was right.

Returning home later that day, I felt the need to pray. Immediately after I closed my eyes, I found myself sitting on the rock overlooking the city. The Archangel sat by my side.

"You are to tell the others," he said.

"I understand," I said, a little impatiently. "But it's been hard for me. I'm trying with the book, but you have to do *your* part."

His expression didn't change with my impudence. "The way of the Lord seems mysterious to you, but it is clear and plain to us. The Lord is preparing the messages and preparing you. You have been sent to the Bible to understand that many of those whom we appeared to were not 'special,' were not 'holy,' but similar to you—ordinary people struggling to find God in their lives. You understand this more clearly, do you not?"

I nodded, thinking back to the passages that had been shown to me. Gideon, of all the people, seemed a lot like me. *How will I do it? Prove to me you're an angel. Show me a sign. Show me another sign.* With each day my faith in the messages strengthened.

"You have questions," the Archangel said, his robe flowing as he moved.

"Yes," I answered. "You must know what it concerns. It's the *none can be saved until all are saved* part. I finally believe it, although I hadn't wanted to for a long time, but I still cannot answer the question people ask me: Why? Why are the good people punished?"

"They are not *punished*," he said. "The Lord is not judgmental. We have told you this before. We asked you to look up the story of the prodigal son, and you did. What did you learn?"

My eyes followed a jet flying above the city. Dawn was breaking and the plane appeared little more than a silver dot in the sky. "I learned," I sighed, "that the lost son, the lost sheep, was welcomed

104

with open arms by his father." Emphatically I added, "And the good son wasn't very happy about it."

The Archangel clasped his hands together as if in prayer. "Christ wants the people to truly understand this parable. The father could never achieve true happiness knowing that his son was still lost. No matter how many riches were afforded him, no matter how good and faithful his other son was, he could not achieve true happiness unless his entire family found their way back home. You must emulate the Father and follow the true, unconditional love that lies within your soul. Until you break open the shell that surrounds your soul and discover the pure love that is God, which is your divinity, you will not rest. You too will not find contentment until your whole family has returned home, returned to God.

"That is true love; that is the love of God. And you will clearly see and feel the divinity around you. You will not find happiness until the whole body finds happiness. Did we not teach you of the whole body in Corinthians?"

I could barely answer. *They* sent me that passage from Sunday's sermon? I had been astounded at the topic. The entire body was one, Paul had written. "Yes," I admitted. "I know the passage."

"The community is essential," the Archangel continued. "The more you grow, the more you will realize that you cannot achieve happiness—you will not want to achieve happiness—as long as others in your community have not returned to God. It will be impossible for you to be truly contented, truly happy, until the entire body faces the Light."

He arose slowly. The mist that had been settling onto the city had disappeared. A large rainbow covered the skyline. "Do you see more clearly?" he asked.

I looked out to the sparkling city. "Yes," I said softly. "I see much more clearly. And it's not what I ever dreamed I would see."

His voice was filled with kindness. "It is beyond your imagination. It is within your soul, it is within the divinity; it is the wisdom of the Spirit. Listen to it; heed it. And become one with each other." He smiled, blessed me, and disappeared.

Though the Archangel had vanished, the rainbow remained. The colors were vibrant and vivid; the city was pale in comparison to God's work. I thanked the Holy Spirit for showing me things that I hadn't realized existed.

And for helping me understand the necessity of community.

Tucking my knees beneath my chin, I drank in the scenery before me. Sunbeams poured through the red, yellow and indigo of the rainbow and the colors reflected onto the city. During the last year, I felt as if I had been struck by lightning, like Saul on the road to Damascus, and was blind before all of this.

Interesting.

The Voice interrupted my thoughts. "Everyone serves a purpose in your journey. Remember the need for each other, the need for the circle of the soul."

Thank you, I whispered, watching the rainbow shimmer in the sky. Mulling over the concept of the Prodigal Son, I began to feel it made some sense. I had thought that if I were to play a character in the story, I would choose the good brother, angry that I lived a fairly decent life and no one killed the calf for me. Now I wasn't so sure.

Things were becoming clearer, but I still had questions about 'none will be saved until all are saved.' Just days before my husband had said to me, "If you don't understand it, ask the Archangel."

"It doesn't work like that," I had answered. "He has his own agenda."

"Well," Tom shrugged, "you won't be much of a messenger if you don't truly understand the message. Ask him. If you get an answer, you'll feel better about all of this."

And today, as I sat on the rock, watching the sky, I heard the Voice begin:

"Such as the body still aches for its missing limb, so will you, like Christ, ache for your missing brothers and sisters. Just as a body without a limb still feels the limb, such will it be without all of the body reunited with God. Christ was in Paradise, yet knew in his heart the sorrow of those still in darkness. Such will it be for you, until all are reunited at Home."

Finally, I understood. *None can be saved until all are saved.*

Simple, I thought. Why hadn't I grasped it before? And then I realized, in my selfishness I could not even have understood the premise: true compassion, true love.

I had so much to learn.

The words gave me enormous comfort. Suddenly many of the messages fell into place. The gifts took on a different nature. They were not only for ourselves but also for each other's salvation.

While I prayed, the Archangel visited me. "As you pray, you will understand that no one will truly find love until they have reunited everyone in the Body with God. True, unconditional love of God is what you must embrace to understand God. When you understand this, you, like Christ, will want everyone to return home. Such is the circle of the soul."

We sat overlooking the city. The rainbow had disappeared and dusk was descending on the city. A light snow was falling rapidly around us, but we were untouched. I pulled my jacket more tightly around my body, yet I felt no chill, no cold. It was as if we were insulated. "I read something in the newspaper today," I mentioned.

"Yes," he said. "It concerned the study of prayer and the community. Does that not confirm what I have been telling you?"

I nodded. The study centered on heart attack victims. Those who prayed and returned to social and community actions healed more quickly than the others.

"The body and the spirit need each other. When you pray, a calming takes effect. When this is combined with love for each other, the purpose of helping and saving each other, more peace resides in you. Did we not tell you that the Spirit feeds the body?"

"Yes," I said, stuffing my hands into my pockets. "You always make this sound so easy, but it is difficult for me."

"What is difficult?" he asked, no hint of impatience or condescension in his voice.

"Believing the messages used to be difficult," I hesitated, "but now, it's living them that is difficult."

"Live as Christ lived. Follow His way, follow His example and the light will beckon to you. With unconditional love you, like Christ, will not want a single sheep to be lost, will not want a single son astray from the fold. You are like mothers, wanting your children to come to you. Stress the need for community and prayer. Understand that true happiness lies, true paradise lies, when all are reunited in God's love."

He continued softly, "It is for each of you to know this. It is for each of you to pray for this. It is for each of you to act upon this and bring each other home. You are dependent on each other for true happiness, for true salvation. How can the father ever be truly content when his prodigal son is lost? Learn to be the father, the mother, who yearns for her children to return. That is the wisdom of the Spirit. The Spirit will show you that love is the answer.

"Follow this love, and pray for the peace which it brings. All is available to you through the Grace of God. Take it. Savor it. Embrace it. Embrace one another's salvation. Pray for one another's salvation."

I said nothing. A blanket of snow, soft and white, had covered the city, muffling its sounds in silence.

"Breathe in the fresh air," the Archangel said. "Breathe in the air of the Spirit. And pray." He made the sign of the cross above me. "Go. Sit in the presence of God."

Chapter Twenty-Two

In the Name of God

A peace had begun to grow within me. I was comfortable with the messages and, more importantly, with the explanations of the messages, which were unfolding before me. Each day I seemed to find more compassion for strangers, for people who were committing horrendous crimes.

But of course I discovered it was easier to have compassion for strangers, people who didn't really impact my life, than for those who had personally wronged me.

How difficult the lessons were to apply! (Even as I write this, the Archangel's words echo in my mind: It is so simple. Walk in faith.)

Sitting down to pray, I was greeted by a small bronze-colored cherub. She was dressed in white robes; her face glowed in innocence. Her voice was childlike, high in tone, as she said, "Come. Come with me."

Before I had a chance to look around for the Archangel, I was transported to the Deep South. The heat was oppressive, the air muggy and thick. In front of us stood men draped in the white robes of the Ku Klux Klan. Many of the men were carrying torches in the shape of crosses. I cringed at the sight and struggled to breathe. In the distance was a parking lot. The cars all seemed recent models, and I realized that the Bronze Cherub had not taken me back in time. The time was now.

"I thought this was something that happened years ago, not

now," I said, watching the men circle on horses, their yelling growing in frenzy.

"It is now," the Bronze Cherub said. "They are performing these hateful acts in the name of God."

Taking hold of my elbow, she brought me to another place. Men wearing turbans, blue and gold, were sitting in the basement of a building. One man was marking a pathway on a map with a large black marker. "They are planning attacks," the Bronze Cherub said sadly, "all in the name of God."

I was silent.

Then we were in lush, green countryside. Immediately I recognized the thick brogue of the people huddled together in a barn. We were in Ireland. Being the equivalent of "flies on the wall," we overheard the group's conversation.

They too were terrorists.

"All in the name of God," the Bronze Cherub said, wiping a tear from her cheek.

"I'm sorry," I said, my words not adequate for the sorrow I felt. "But what can *I* do?"

We stood in the middle of the barn, smelling the fresh-mown hay stacked in the corner and listening to the plans of bombings.

"They are performing these hideous crimes all in the name of God. By using His name they believe they can condone and justify the atrocities that are committed on a daily basis. This is not the God of Love. This is not our God," the Bronze Cherub said softly. "These people," she said with a sweep of her hand, "are using the name like a pagan god, a god of material possession, a god of land acquisitions and power." She sighed, her eyes riveted on the small group. "Ours is a beautiful and loving God."

"Yes," I said. "I understand. But one person is helpless against such evil."

"Pray," she said, turning toward me. "And tell the community which faces the light to pray for those in darkness. The power of the community's prayer will override such horrendous plans." She clasped her hands together. "Pray for your enemies. Pray for those in darkness. Such prayer will save you and the others."

The barn became stiflingly hot. The voices of the group rose in anger. My head pounded, and I tugged at the Bronze Cherub's sleeve. "Could you please take me home?" Beside me men were divvying up territories to bomb. I didn't want to hear any more.

She raised her eyebrows. "When the messages are pleasant, you are willing to listen to us. But when they show you the reality of the world, that you are responsible for the others, you no longer care to hear them."

I looked away.

"You are your sister," she said, taking me by the shoulders and pointing me in the direction of the small group. I had no other choice but to stare at them. "You are your brother. You are capable of such atrocities, but you must face the light, pray for the others, and ask the community as a whole to pray. That power is the strongest."

She flew up slightly, kissed me on the forehead, and smiled. I smelled the sweet smell of lilies of the valley.

"Transcribe this," she said, her tone serious. "Pray, and let it be known. *Holy Spirit, please send me the wisdom that You so freely offer. Let me understand that the knowledge is in loving God and each other. Fill me with that wisdom, the wisdom of love and compassion. Let me be a vehicle for prayer. Allow me to hold the light. Shine it on my path and the path of others. Let me forgo the darkness, the doubt, and show me the wisdom which is Yours.*"

With that, she made the sign of the cross and departed.

This time *I* wiped away the tear.

Chapter Twenty-Three

Courage

The day was glorious. I ran along the warm beach, feeling the hot grains of sand beneath my bare feet. I climbed the rock awkwardly, hurrying to sit next to the Archangel. The sun streamed down upon us, his navy robes shining in the brilliant rays.

I settled down next to him, happy to be there.

With little greeting the Archangel opened his large golden staff. Diamonds tumbled onto the rock and sands. "Please," he said, his blue eyes deeper than the ocean next to us, "select one."

I reached into a crevice of the rock and picked up a large gem. At first it seemed pink, but in my hand it turned a deep dark purple. The stone was warm, from the sun or perhaps just its own heat. I held it tightly and felt a pulse, almost a heartbeat, come from it. "It's pulsating," I said, wrapping my fingers around it more tightly.

"It is alive," he said. "It is courage. Take it. These gifts come freely from God. During these times, like many people, you need courage."

"Courage?" I asked, holding the stone up and closely examining it.

"Yes," he said. "Even though you have heard these messages, you need the courage to continue to hold them close to you."

"Why do I always find it so hard?" I whined.

"Because you are not walking completely in faith. You think that only holy people or saints can live these messages. But we assure you, all can live in the state of unconditional love."

He was right. I didn't think I was capable of following the messages. How could I love and pray for my neighbor? How could I have compassion for strangers and enemies? It all seemed beyond my selfish ways.

"Courage is necessary for many. Doubt, anxiety and fear still easily take hold of you. These are temptations from darkness. You find them easy to embrace because they comfort you. It is a pattern that must be broken. Only God's gifts and your prayers can accomplish this task."

I fingered the stone. It was heavy, solid, but brilliant.

"Do not be afraid. Do not worry. All is simple when you are walking on God's path."

I took a deep breath. Whenever I was sitting here, next to this angel who had become my friend, I felt ready to take on the world. But when he left....

"Do not rely on us," he said, as if reading my thoughts. "We are only messengers of His word. It is God and His gifts that you need to hold fast to. Courage must fight the evil that lurks in the world. Courage must abolish the fears that surround you. Fear will separate you from God, from the wisdom of the Spirit, from the love of Christ. When fear and anxiety begin to take hold, cast them out and hold fast to the courage that is God's gift. Within your soul, you yearn to return home to God, to be reunited with God and each other. Remember that and do not let the fears of the world, the fears of the body, hold you from your true path."

I exhaled deeply, feeling lighter.

"Allow the toxins which form in your body to leave. Continue to breathe out, forcing the anxiety out of your body. Pray to the Lord as you do it. Remember, the shell that forms around the spirit grows thicker with fear and worldly concerns. Many of the diseases of the body come from not allowing the spirit to truly live. Listen to the Spirit, and the body will be free of anxiety. Many of the diseases that plague you will disappear. Faith and confidence in the divine will assure your body of calmness and serenity."

My eyes were locked on the Archangel.

"You can choose to be either in a circle of love, which frees the spirit and heals the body, or a circle of fear and darkness, which imprisons the soul and sickens the body. The choice is yours because God has given you freedom."

He paused slightly, adding, "But the only true choice is the one of love. Eventually you will all understand this."

"Take this courage," he said, resting his hand over the gem that I was holding. "Hold it fast and remember the strength which all of God's gifts offer. When fear and anxiety beckon to you, hold fast to the courage which is the peace of the Lord." He smiled at me. "Remember that love will result in peace. Darkness will result in anxiety. It is all so simple."

Closing my fingers over the gem, I prayed silently that I could hold onto it.

The Archangel added, "When you feel anxiety, or hate for another, pray for the other. Then peace for your own body and soul will result."

As I watched the Archangel disappear into the sky, he called out: "Pray. Pray every day and tell the others. Such will connect you to the peace of God. Such will allow the circle of the souls to reunite."

Chapter Twenty-Four

The Cycle of Sin

I woke up in a cold sweat. Sitting up, I searched around the bed trying to find my husband's back. I rested my hand against its warmth, trying to compose myself.

The nightmare had been so realistic it had shaken me to the core. In the dream I had committed a horrible crime. I didn't remember what had happened, but I knew it was horrific. As I sat in the darkness of our bedroom, I heard the Voice, clear and strong, say to me: "Listen to this dream and see the cycle of sin. It can be broken."

When morning came I sat down to pray. The Archangel appeared quickly. This time we were on the roof of an apartment building. I sat atop some type of cement block as we overlooked the city twelve stories below. Our vantage point was much closer than our other view of the city; I could clearly make out the clothes of the people walking below us. It was dawn, and the city was already bustling.

The Archangel wore a deep rose-colored robe, and an aura of pink and yellow surrounded him. "Did you feel the dream last night?" he asked.

"I don't remember it very clearly," I answered. "All I remember is the feeling of hopelessness, the feeling that I would never get out of the trouble. I would be forever banished and marked for my crime."

"That is the feeling we wanted you to experience," he said calmly.

"Explain it in more detail."

Wanted me to experience? I shook my head. "It was a mixture of feelings. I was so sorry for the crime, embarrassed, exhausted, and although I don't remember what the crime was, I remember trying to cover it up. I remember a profound feeling of terror, despair and shame."

He opened his hands. The stigmata on his palms faced upward. "There is a cycle of sin," the Archangel said. "One sin leads to another. Embarrassment and shame soon set in. Soon the soul cannot climb out of this dark well. The person sees nothing but the sin and the walls surrounding it. He is so deep into this well of despair that the light is only a faded memory. Without the light, cold, darkness and dampness penetrate his soul. He begins to live and breathe the sin and darkness."

I agreed, remembering the feeling of total despair, the people talking and pointing at me. I remembered wanting to die to end the misery.

The Archangel rested his hand on my upper back. "This despair from which people suffer, this sin which they think is inescapable, is easily washed away." He opened his golden staff. "Christ came to break this cycle of sin. He came to show those rooted in the dark well that the light is always beckoning. He came to forgive their sins." The Archangel looked at me, his deep blue eyes filled with sadness. "Why do people forget this?" From within his staff he removed a wonderfully round diamond. It reminded me of a crystal baseball. The Archangel rolled it between his palms. When he stopped, I noticed his stigmata had faded slightly.

"This is the gift of forgiveness," he said quietly, his eyes never leaving the gem. "It is available from God. Christ brought it to earth and the sins of the people were forgiven. It is for everyone to accept from God. Their sins are forgiven; they are to forgive others."

He held up the diamond as a priest holds up a communion host. Spectrums of vivid colors flashed from the stone. It appeared almost alive and pulsating. "It is a great and magnificent gift," the

Archangel said. "Despair and darkness are banished by this gift."

I reached to touch the glittering diamond. Warmth flowed from it to my fingertips. "It's beautiful," I murmured, not knowing what else to say.

"Christ's gift to the world, God's gift to the world," he said, gently lowering the gem. The Archangel looked at me intently. "People must accept such a magnificent gift. It is important that they embrace this forgiveness, and it is equally as important that they use it to forgive each other. As Christ said, `Forgive us our sins, as we forgive each other.' That is the gift of forgiveness. As each of you turns toward the light, God in his mercy allows your path to clear and the way home to be seen. You must use this gift with each other."

My eyes were riveted on the large diamond. Colors seemed to flow out of it, like beams from a lighthouse.

"Pray for those deep within the well to see the light, to reach for the light," he continued. "Forgive them their transgressions, as God has forgiven you. Remember to tell everyone that accepting God's gifts can easily break the cycle of sin. Nothing is hopeless. There can be no despair in the light of God. Remember this. Forgive each other and pray for each other, and the pathway home will be clearly marked."

Below us I heard the sound of screeching tires. Turning to look, I saw a traffic jam and police car. I stuttered, "This whole experience is sometimes rather difficult for me, you know..." Here he was talking about lofty ideals, and I was thinking of myself.

"We understand," the Archangel said. "But we have given you time; we have given you messages. Listen to the events we send you. Have faith in God's plan. Remember what the Voice told you yesterday."

Oh dear, I thought. I had already forgotten it. I felt so stupid.

"You wrote it down," the Archangel said, like a mother prodding her child to find homework. "Go, find it, and transcribe it."

I remembered writing something down. Looking through my purse, sure enough, I found it. In the pages of my memo book I had scribbled, "When you have embraced the unconditional love of God, no one will choose to leave another behind. You will ache for your brothers and sisters, as Christ ached for you. This is the message of the One; this is the message of the community. Listen to it, and live it."

"Oh, we're back to this," I said. "None will be saved until all are saved."

"Yes," he said, a slight smile on his face, "because when you embrace and experience God's love, you will want everyone else to experience it also. Live this message. Embrace the forgiveness that Christ brought with him. Pass this gift on to your neighbor."

When I had initially met the Archangel, over a year ago, my heart would beat wildly at some of the meetings. This morning it happened again. I pressed my hand against my chest, looked at the Archangel, and wondered about my sanity.

As if he read my mind, he replied. "You wondered about these messages, but they are from God. They speak only of loving God and your neighbor. That is the essence. Do not fear them. Hold them tightly to your soul and tell the others of them. All know this within their souls, but the souls are locked in a prison of doubt, anxiety and darkness. Crack open the shell and the love will return you home."

As I studied his face, chiseled yet kind, my heart stopped racing. His blue eyes reminded me of the depths of the ocean, holding discoveries far beyond my reach.

"You were concerned that angels appeared only to Biblical, holy figures. Hasn't that fear vanished?"

I nodded, thinking back to the times of despair and doubt when I opened the Bible at random. Once I opened it to Judges 6:11, where I read about Gideon constantly questioning an angel. Another time I was brought to Jonah, who refused to hear God's message and ended up inside a whale. I had been led to scores of such passages, all teaching me that angels came to ordinary people, many of whom were sinners, not saints. It gave me comfort.

"You are not special," the Archangel said.

I lowered my gaze.

He continued. "As many of those people were not special. But they, like you, were willing to listen to these messages. Now the challenge lies in accepting the gifts. If only you understood how simple is the pathway to God! Break the cycle of despair and darkness and walk toward the light of hope and optimism."

As we gazed down at the city below, I heard a gunshot and saw a woman fall to the ground.

"Pray," the Archangel said softly. "Pray for the perpetrator to face the light of the Lord."

I did, but still I prayed for the woman on the ground.

I was back in my living room, but like so many other times, the Voice still held me fast.

"Tell the others of the importance of community and the importance of giving and receiving forgiveness. Everything is a circle. Think of Christ, think of love, and that circle returns to you. Begin with despair and that darkness will encompass you. Turn toward the light and give off the light. That is the message. Like a flower absorbing the minerals from the ground, absorb God's love and light, and in turn you will reflect this to the others. It is a circle of souls, and you are to help one another.

"The gifts of God are available to all. What you do to the least of my brothers you do unto me, Christ said. Remember that; it is a circle of salvation. And none will be saved, none will find true happiness, until all are saved."

I softly added an "amen."

I started to stand up, assuming the session was over. But the Archangel appeared again, beckoning to me, and we were standing near a woman whose purse had been stolen. A kind passerby was kneeling next to her, helping her to sit up. Beside the woman, obviously invisible to the crowd, was a large angel, her wings spread over the woman's body. Slowly the woman rose to her feet; she appeared unharmed.

"Come," the Archangel said. "There is more."

I hesitated.

"Come," he said firmly.

Immediately we were sitting in a decrepit cellar. I breathed in the smell of dirt, mold and urine. Covering my nose, I still could not get the odor of the basement out of my nostrils. As I looked around, I saw the purse of the woman who had been mugged; it was open, tossed on the floor.

Nearby a small group of people, all ages and colors, passed a common needle to each other. In the middle of this group sat the man who had mugged the woman.

I turned away. "Take me home."

The Archangel appeared not to hear my request. "See them?" he asked.

"Take me home," I insisted.

"Pray for them," he continued, "for your heart should ache with sadness."

I closed my eyes. My heart did ache, but still I did not want to *see* these people, *see* this life.

"You are he," the Archangel continued, as if deaf to my pleas, "He is you. It is a circle of the souls. Pray for one another and you will save each other through God's kindness and compassion."

Within seconds I was back home. I exhaled, as if trying to assure myself I was breathing. Some days all of this seemed too much for me.

"We understand," the Voice said clearly. "Walk slowly and with confidence toward the light of God. It will serve as a beacon for you and soon you will run toward it. You will want to help each other, because you will see the results of unconditional love. You will feel the love encompass your soul. "

I silently thanked the Voice, but wanted to rest.

"Community," the Voice said. "Community of the souls. Christ ached for your redemption, as all of you will ache for the redemption of each other."

"Thank you," I said tiredly, wondering *how* to accomplish these tasks.

"Through prayer," the Voice answered. "Through prayer and acceptance of God's gifts. Walk toward the love which calls to you."

Chapter Twenty-Five

A Simple Walkway

One afternoon I met with my writers' group. These women had all read *Songs of the Soul* and many of them had helped me edit and polish it. This particular day we were discussing a horrendous crime that had taken place a few weeks before. A woman had drowned her two children. Many people wanted the woman to receive the death penalty; people were in an uproar.

My friend asked me my opinion. I mumbled that I had been praying for the woman. *Was this really I speaking?* I, who had believed in capital punishment, I who had followed the creed of "an eye for an eye"?

Another woman asked, "Would you have done that before the book?"

I shook my head. I was both ashamed at my previous behavior and shocked at my new one. I would have been the first person to scream for the mother's execution. Now, I saw it differently. We were supposed to pray for those in darkness.

On the way home from this meeting, I thought about the difference these messages had made in my spiritual life. I had begun to notice that it was easier to pray than to get angry. Changes were taking place within me, and they surprised me.

As I sat down to pray, I tried awkwardly to find the right words. Praying for guidance, I asked help to stop worrying over concerns about material security. I prayed that God would help me focus on the more important things in life.

The Voice answered, quite clearly: "I will fill your heart with goodness and plenty."

I repeated the sentence in my mind, wondering what it meant.

Soon afterward, the Archangel greeted me on the beach. The shore had become my favorite meeting spot. It was nighttime and stars filled the sky. I watched the constellations glitter. It was gorgeous and I was grateful to be sitting there, next to my friend. The Archangel wore a dark tawny robe, which gleamed in the moonlight.

"What are we going to talk about today?" I asked, settling on top of the rock.

"You must pray," he said somberly, "alone, in the presence of the Lord. You are not doing this and it is essential."

"It's hard for me," I said. "My thoughts wander. I see only darkness, and hear even less."

"You will find the truth in His presence. You will find peace in His presence. Do this and follow the Lord."

"I'll try," I answered meekly.

"Good," he said, unfolding his hands.

"But you must help me," I continued, not letting the subject end so easily.

"We will," he said, his eyes filled with kindness as he spoke. "But it is your individual path, your individual communication with God that is necessary."

I said nothing.

"We realize that you find this difficult, but all of these tasks are methods for you to move toward the light of the world. They are simple, ordinary tasks that hold wonderment, peace and love. Sit and listen to your soul and visit with the Lord, and the peace of the Spirit will reside within you. You will break open the shell that smothers your soul and find everlasting love and life. All of this is available to everyone. The spirit is eager to help everyone find this wisdom from God. Implore and pray. It shall be given to you."

He continued speaking, his voice firm over the sound of the rolling waves. "Remember that all of these messages will bring you an easier way of life, an easier path, a simple walkway toward the Lord and the divinity which resides within each of you. Remember that Christ so loved the world that He gave His life for His brothers and sisters. Such will be all of your love for each other. Christ ached for your redemption; you too will ache for the redemption of all. Remember these words," he concluded. "Live them and heed them."

"Amen," I whispered, watching a shooting star fall to the ground. It shot out of the darkness and traveled quickly. I wondered if the other stars ached for its loss.

Later that afternoon, the Voice announced, "Christ is the Way. As you become like Christ, you follow the way to the Lord, the way home."

I heard it, pondered it for a moment, and then returned to cleaning out my closets. Even with my shoes strewn on the floor, I had trouble concentrating on the task at hand. The message kept repeating in my mind. I felt compelled to sit again and pray. Somewhat reluctantly, I glanced back at the pile of clothing and walked downstairs.

The Archangel immediately greeted me back at the beach. He held a small stone in his hand. It was quite ordinary, not shiny or brilliant like the other gems. It was dark, almost black, and oblong. He fingered it lightly.

"What is that?" I asked.

He extended his hand. "Stillness."

I touched the top of the stone. I liked the cool smooth texture against my skin.

"Please take it," he said. "It is a gift."

I accepted it, rubbing it between my palms.

"You must still your mind, which you are having difficulty doing, in order to listen to God's whispers, in order to listen to the sweet messages of the soul. In this stillness you will hear the Way, you will hear the Word, and you will hear the others. You will be able to help the others, and thus yourself, while immersed in this stillness. In the confusion of your world, with the noise, the doubt, the troubles that surround you, you cannot hear the soul crying out for release. You cannot hear the knowledge that it holds because you are following a worldly agenda. When this occurs, savor the stillness, turn toward the light, disperse the darkness and find comfort in the voice of God. His voice will call to you; it will beckon to you. The Spirit will show you wisdom; will demonstrate knowledge. With this understanding you will be able to walk the Way."

I clutched the stone.

"The light will shine fiercely on you, illuminating your darkness. The stillness will not be frightening if you face the Lord."

The waves were crashing nearby and the air was clear and salty and wonderful. I opened my mouth, trying to taste it.

"Do not let your mind wander to the worldly," he said, almost chastising me for focusing on the ocean. "There is a time for the sea. There is a time to appreciate nature and find God in His creations. Yet in order to find the stillness you must go within, not without."

I snapped my mouth closed and shut my eyes. In the background I heard the ocean rumbling and felt a wind gently caressing my feet.

"In the stillness," he said patiently, "hold onto this gem. Hold it; focus on it. Feel its density and enter the density of your mind. There you will find the Lord. In the peace that resides within you, you will find communication with your soul, with the divine. Please do this for your journey. Your journey will progress and you will be brought closer to the light."

"Thank you," I said, opening my eyes. I knew that finding the stillness of which he spoke would be difficult for me, but I would try. I grasped the stone more tightly. Looking down, I noticed it was not a gem at all, but rather just a rock, a common beach rock.

"All of God's creations are gems," said the Archangel, smiling. "Did you just discover this?"

"Yes," I admitted ashamedly. "Yes."

"In the most common of His creations you can find peace. You can find the beauty that He gives to you and the caring which He pours upon you. All of this is for the world, but the most beautiful is within you."

"Oh."

"Go," he said, raising his arms toward the sky. "Go into the stillness of your soul. There you will find God. You will understand His plans for you. You will understand the circle of the souls through the knowledge of the spirit. Everyone must take time to pray in this fashion." He turned his palms upward toward the heavens. "Pray to learn to be a vehicle and container for the Word. Release your soul and listen to the Spirit."

Chapter Twenty-Six

Forget the Transgressions

I had tossed and turned much of the night. Dawn was peeping through the shades as I tried to get back to sleep, but I could not. Frustrated, I tried to meditate. The Voice interrupted my feeble attempts. "You are to dismiss the worrisome thoughts," it said. "Let them pass like floating clouds."

I tried, but to no avail.

"We are to teach you how to sit in the presence of God," the Voice continued.

I sat up.

"We are to teach you forgiveness and forgetting."

Desperately I tried to sit in the presence of the Lord, tried to allow the "worrisome" thoughts no room in my mind. But it didn't seem to work. My mind wanted to take me to the day's activities: The alarm would be going off soon. Breakfast needed to be made. The sheets needed changing.

How would I ever learn to pray quietly, to sit in the presence of the Lord?

I got up, went downstairs, and made a pot of coffee.

Later that morning I sat down to pray. Within seconds the Archangel appeared to me. We were sitting at the banks of a river, watching the water rush past us. The forest surrounding us was a lush dark green. I inhaled deeply, smelling that delightful mixture of forest, pine and new grass.

The Archangel sat on the rock ledge next to me and began

speaking. "Everything is a circle. A circle of souls."

I listened.

"Your bodies and souls are connected. As you turn from the light, you become anxious. When this anxiety takes hold of your body, it thickens the shell around your soul. The body begins to take precedence for you. You worry about your bodily and worldly concerns and then ignore the spirit. Thus the spirit begins to suffocate. When the spirit is not able to be free, the body is not nourished.

"And the opposite," he continued, "is true. When the body turns toward God, and is not anxious about worldly concerns, the soul is allowed to come to the surface. The spiritual concerns take precedence. Thus the body is calm and the worldly concerns become secondary. Each affects the other.

"Turn toward the light," he urged me.

I saw a small fish jump from the water, and then noticed as others followed. Turning my gaze back to the Archangel, I said, "I know what you're saying, but you don't understand this." I paused, trying to find the right words. "I don't mean to be difficult, although I know I am, but I have an awful time not worrying, not being concerned about the things which affect my day-to-day life."

I took a big breath before continuing. "And I also worry about these messages. How can I, one unknown woman, get them out? I've done my best, but it doesn't seem good enough."

"God is with you. Do not concern yourself. Everything has a plan. Everything has a cycle and a harvest. Let these words take root within you. Then you may harvest them and share them with the community. Do not rush the season. Do not rush the plans of God."

I pondered this for a moment, reluctantly agreeing with him. "But how do I *stop* worrying?"

He sighed and made the sign of the cross over the river.

"Pray and practice the meditations which we have taught to you. Dismiss the cares from the body and turn toward the gift of stillness which God has given to you. That stillness will feed your body and free your soul."

"Okay," I said half-heartedly. Hadn't I tried that before? But to no avail.

"Do not rush," the Archangel said. "Take time with the silence."

He took my hand and patted it. Rarely did he give me that kind of personal touch. "You have been like a snowball, slowly over the centuries rolling forward on the ground. And now, suddenly, the movement has strengthened and you feel like an avalanche picking up speed."

I disagreed. "I feel like I'm not getting anywhere."

He smiled. "With each person who realizes that each is one with the others, the pathway toward God moves faster. You are moving, unbeknownst to yourself, through the grace and goodness of God."

I dipped my feet into the rushing water. It was cold but not frigid.

"Let us talk of forgetting," the Archangel said.

"Okay." That sounded harmless.

"You must not only forgive each other, but you must forget the transgressions."

I pulled my feet out of the water.

"Christ, through his redemption, forgot yours, as if a slate were wiped clean. Now it is up to each of you to turn toward the light that beckons you home. But you, too, must forgive and forget the hurts from your neighbor."

The Archangel reached down, and then held up a clump of dirt. Clenching his fist, he crumbled the soil, allowing it to fall through his open fingers. "Such as this represents the offense, such must you break it apart, forgive the transgressor, allow the deed to be taken away toward God, to be forgiven and forgotten in His Light."

His action reminded me of a priest holding up the communion chalice.

I shook my head. "It's not so easy. Perhaps I can forgive some-one, but how will I ever *forget*? How will I ever forget the·hurt which they inflicted on me?" I bit my lower lip, and watched an eel slither down the embankment.

"Christ has forgotten yours. You must forget your neighbor's."

I swallowed hard.

"That is the lesson. The lesson is to forget the debts. Any negative memories you harbor within will fester, and the act of forgiveness will not be truthful. Clear the deeds from your mind, as God has done for you. In finding the way home, you must live as Christ lived. You must realize that all are one. If you do not forget someone else's transgressions, yours will not be forgotten, and the negativity which this harbors will reside in you like a cancer, eating away the positive light-filled cells."

He scowled at me, and a cloud covered the sky. "Can you understand this?"

"Yes," I said, my voice becoming emphatic. "But you're asking a lot of us. We're only human."

"Your bodies are human. Your souls are divine," he replied.

I closed my eyes. He always had an answer for my arguments.

"Ask your soul to guide your life. Ask the Helper to give you wisdom, and all of these edicts will be easily accomplished. The Helper gives you the wisdom that you seek and unlocks your souls from their imprisonment. With this wisdom your bodies will flourish easily.

"Pray for wisdom. Pray for the Helper to bless you with knowledge."

I took hold of his hand and traced the sign of the stigmata with my fingertip. My own stigmata began to throb. I gripped his hand more tightly. "You have asked a lot of me. I still think that perhaps you've got the wrong woman. Maybe you should have called on someone who will get the job done, someone who could get the messages out better than I have."

"You are 'getting the job done,' as you say. You are walking in faith with this message."

I didn't agree.

"Have you not been shown Bible passages?" the Archangel asked.

I nodded. I had never been much of a Bible reader, but since these visits I had turned to the Bible many times.

"Were you not shown Jeremiah? Were you not shown Gideon? Jonah?" the Archangel continued.

"Yes," I answered humbly, recalling each of the instances vividly. When I had desperately fought the messages, making excuses (I'm not holy, I'm not good enough, I can't spread these words, and most especially—am I crazy?), I had randomly opened the Bible to Jeremiah. He had found every excuse in the world not to spread God's word. I discovered that excuses were just part of being human. The important lesson was ignoring the excuses and listening to God. Gideon was a man after my own heart. He always wanted another sign—just to make sure.

And another time, needing assurance, I had opened the Bible to the story of Jonah. As a child I remembered only that Jonah lived inside a whale for days. But as an adult I learned the circumstances of that situation.

Jonah had been asked to spread God's word, and he had refused to do it. He did not want the Assyrians, his enemies, to be saved. Jonah did not intend to teach them God's word even though God had instructed him to do just that. He fled from God's request. He went to the sea, as if trying to escape his responsibility. The ship rocked, the storm raged, and the other sailors finally threw Jonah into the ocean. He was saved from drowning when a whale swallowed him, and he spent three days and three nights inside its belly.

I knew the feelings Jonah experienced. I understood not wanting to save the criminals, the horribly evil people. And oftentimes, I had fled from my responsibilities.

Each time, God saved me.

The Archangel smiled at me. "These people were common people who had difficulty accepting the word of God. They were ordinary, scared, no different than you, and they did not want the responsibility. Did not Gideon say he was the lowest in his family?"

"Yes."

"Well, you are not different. You are ordinary, a sinner. You too are capable of hateful deeds and of turning away from God. But during this period you have faced Him and are listening to His Word, however reluctantly. Therefore, do not think that you are crazy and do not think that you are special. Just do as you are instructed and let the others know that to find paradise they must turn toward God and each other. They must live as Christ lived, follow the Way, and realize that the Body of Christ is a living, moving element. They must realize that without each other, they will never reach fulfillment."

The Archangel made the sign of the cross over the river, and disappeared into the cloudless sky.

As I stared at the cool running waters, the fish jumped. They looked as if they were playing, celebrating life.

The Voice spoke to me. "That is the way God wants you to live your life. Follow the flow of the river, enjoy the waters, and do not be concerned with the worldly. Head home to God, raising your faces to the warm light that illuminates the path. Forget anxiety and doubts. Rush toward the Lord in love and peace."

My "Amen" was barely audible over the running river.

Chapter Twenty-Seven

Your Choice

On Saturdays my routine was different. I hadn't prayed in the morning. I had had a leisurely breakfast with my husband and then got caught up watching some old movie on cable television.

Later on Tom went to get his hair cut, and I was alone in the house. I thought of sitting and praying, but I had a lot of errands to get done before he returned.

And then the Voice said: "You must pray every day."

You must pray every day.

The Archangel appeared by the riverbank. I cast my eyes down, ashamed at my behavior.

"Unconditional love," he began, "is selfless. True love holds no reins, nor harbors ill will. It flows powerfully and freely from the river of the soul. Christ had this love for you, as you must for your neighbors. Your soul will soar with the freedom that comes from discarding fears, selfishness and doubts. Your soul will move toward the message which Christ brought to this earth."

As he spoke I was not absorbing all of his words. "It is irrelevant," he said when I asked him to slow down. "It is the emotion of love which will endure forever, not the mere words. People must pray, and with this prayer, with this love, an emotion within them will take flight. Words are meaningless when this love is experienced."

I felt worse. I wasn't even close to his way of thinking.

"You are nearer than you think. All of you have this love within you and around you, but you do not see it, you do not feel it. You concentrate only on things which you can see."

"Come," he said, extending his hand. "Come along with me."

I took his hand, somewhat apprehensively, and immediately we were on a war-torn street. If I were to guess, I would say it was Bosnia. On the deserted street, surrounded by blown-out buildings, a small boy cried over his mother's dead body. Her torso was blown away, but the boy did not leave her side, alternately crying out his mother's name and calling for help.

Before we could step closer the scenery changed. The climate was torrid and tropical. The Archangel and I stood inside a small tin-roofed shanty. On a cot a man lay bleeding to death. He had been beaten in the head; his face was beyond recognition. Without needing to be told, I knew his employer had done this to him.

"Help him," I implored the angel.

"Pray, and God will assist him. But it is not for me alone to help. I must listen to the prayers of the people. With prayers, I gain strength."

I shook my head. There wasn't enough time.

"This man will survive," the Archangel said, making the sign of the cross over his head, "and not be caught up in a vindictive hate. But there are many people all over the world who are caught in this web of hate. Few see the senselessness of it."

I slouched against the tin wall.

"The world is only material. Eternity, a time filled with love, stretches ahead of you. But first you must capture this love within yourselves. You must practice love to fully understand its magnitude."

I watched the man's wife and daughter wash the blood from his skull. He stirred slightly, crying out in pain.

"Take me home," I said sharply. "I've had enough. You always show me the horrors of the world. You hardly ever show me anything good."

He shook his head, as if in disbelief. He waved his hand over the sad scene. "This is the message. The beautiful is with you always. The divine is always shown to you. It is your choice—*your choice*—to see what you want to see. You do not choose to see the beauty of God, the divinity within each of you. You turn away, because it is not material." His voice became even stronger. "But it is more solid than anything of this earth. Do not forget this. Open your eyes and see the beauty of the love that is around you. The circle of souls is the most beautiful sight on this earth, and yet many are blind to it, as blind as Saul on the road to Damascus. But soon your eyes will open and you will see the world the way it was originally, bathed in God's love."

"My eyes are open," I said tiredly. "I've learned the things you've taught me. You told me that we are all one, and I believe that now. Can't we just stop there?"

"No," he said, "because that is not the end of your lesson. The beauty that surrounds you must be seen and experienced. You must release it from your souls and truly love your neighbor. These prayers will result in actions, the actions of God through you."

The heat in the small hut had become oppressive. I wiped the perspiration from my face.

The Archangel continued. "You will not listen any more today. You are tired and confused."

"Yes," I said, ashamed to be both.

"Let these lessons take root in your heart," he continued. "Remember that love is unending and monumental. The soul magnifies this love. A community facing God is powerful. You are all to reunite, and return this love to God."

"Like a present?" I asked, visualizing the world wrapping up the love and handing it to God.

"It will be the greatest gift you can give."

He brought me back to the beach, though we had started out at the riverbank. I savored the light breeze and cawing of the seagulls. The waves crashed at my feet, and I inhaled the salt air deeply. I called out for the Archangel, but he had disappeared.

I dug my toes into the sands. Although I could not see my dear friend, I heard his voice over the sea. "Breathe in the Spirit. The Holy Spirit is just waiting to give all of you the wisdom that was promised. Only ask and the Spirit will pour forth. Amen."

"Amen," I echoed, digging my heels deeper into the warm comforting sand.

Chapter Twenty-Eight

Never Ending Gifts

The beach was warm and sunny, a far cry from the cold February weather which actually surrounded my home. I sat down on the rock, eagerly awaiting the Archangel's arrival.

But the Voice spoke from the clouds. "Prayer results in action, and the actions will be made simple."

I strained to see beyond the clouds.

The Voice continued. "You see with the eyes of the material body, and see only the body. You must see with the eyes of the soul and view the true reality, the body of the spiritual, the body of the spirit, the body of Christ."

I didn't reply.

"God answers readily the selfless prayers you pray for others," the Voice went on.

My own voice was small and barely audible as I asked, "But what about the prayers I pray for myself?"

"They are always heard," the Voice answered kindly, "but the requests for you by your brothers and sisters are very powerful. Such is the circle of the souls."

The circle of the souls.

"These are the lessons of the circle of the souls. You will save your brothers and sisters; they will save you. The body of Christ will be made whole again, and this love will be given as a gift to the Lord. It will be never ending."

The Voice stopped, and the Archangel appeared at the far end of the beach. Hurriedly I climbed down from the rock and ran toward him. His jeweled staff gleamed brilliantly in the sunlight.

"You must pray every day," he said.

Catching my breath, I sputtered, "I'm trying."

"You must be quiet and worship the Lord."

I knew he was right. Why didn't I always do it? It seemed so overwhelming at times, and I felt so tired. Why did the Archangel even bother with me?

"Do not fear," he said, resting his hand on my shoulder. Strength and energy poured into me at his touch.

"Why do I always falter?" I asked. "You tell me these wonderful, beautiful things and I hold onto them for a while, but then I get caught up in my own worries. You keep telling me this is a spiritual journey, but *you're* not in a body." I paused, trying to gather the right words. "My friend has a horrible disease. It's a terminal type of leukemia. No matter what you tell me about the spiritual, she struggles every day just to stay alive. Each morning she wakes up hoping that her disease was just a horrible nightmare." My voice had gotten louder as I continued. "But it's not!"

The Archangel folded his arms together, gently tucking them beneath the robes that covered his chest. "What has she told you about this disease?" he asked.

I avoided his gaze. "She's told me that she has a whole new outlook on life, that the most important things are her family and the love which surrounds her."

The Archangel did not comment.

I turned back, and screamed. "But can't you teach us these lessons without all of this horrible pain? Can't we just understand all of this without going through all this hell?"

He barely moved. "Your mind creates this hell. It creates this heaven. Heaven can be on earth. All is within your grasp. You can hold fast to God, believe in love, and practice the Way. When these anxieties are put aside in the faith of God, a true peace will surround you. Then you will not be in this 'hell' as you call it. Turn toward the light and you will turn toward peace. You are capable of making this choice. This choice is yours. God gave you this free will. *You can choose this heaven. You can choose this peace which is constantly around and within you.*"

I clenched my fist and began to cry, slumping into the damp sand. "I can't!" I said. "I try and try and try, but I still can't do it."

"You are on the road," he said gently, reaching down to take my hand. "You have realized much in the last year. With these realizations has come prayer for your sisters and brothers, and with this prayer comes action. Prayer will bring peace to the world, to each of you."

I stood up, brushing sand from my legs.

The Archangel opened his staff, letting a handful of gems fall to the ground. "We have given you many gifts which will help you on this journey toward peace." He took a gem and placed it in my palm. "Here is serenity."

"You already gave me serenity, a long time ago," I answered.

"You held it only shortly," he said sadly, "and lost it. Take it again. The gifts are never ending. There is a limitless supply."

I touched the diamond.

"The Lord's love, patience and gifts are constant. Remember this and hold fast to these words."

"Thank you," I said, barely able to get the words out through my tears. "I'm so sorry that I've lost so many of the gifts."

He smiled. "Remember, they are limitless."

I smiled back.

"Go," he said, making the sign of the cross over my forehead. "Pray for one another and live in the light of the Lord."

Chapter Twenty-Nine

Do Not Spin Within Your Own Web

The next day wind and snow whipped around us as the Archangel and I sat overlooking the city. Even though I never felt cold, I wanted to leave. But the Archangel and I sat there, throughout the night and into the dawn, just watching the clean white snow descend upon the land. Although we did not talk I felt a peace and quiet that had been escaping me for some time.

Finally he returned me to the warm sunny beach. I had come to realize that at the shore the messages were more personal; in the city they were more community-centered.

"You are too concerned with your own problems, your own development," he said, shaking his head. His white robe shone in the sun, almost blinding me with its purity. "You do not realize that by helping and praying for others, your own problems will be resolved.

"This is the message: Do not dwell on your own problems, your own concerns, because they will not be rectified in that manner. As I have told you before, the more you concentrate on the negative, the more it will grow, and the same is true for the positive. People try to analyze their souls, analyze their problems, but the truth is that in helping others through situations, their own problems will be minimized and eradicated. This is the message of love and community. Do not spin within your own web. Move outward toward the community, toward one another, and help your neighbor. When this is truly accomplished you will be aiding another, and the other will be aiding you. Then the circle of the souls will be empowered and connected. This is the goal; this is the way it was meant to be. When you selfishly concentrate on yourselves, the plan does not move, the energy does not move toward God. Everything becomes stagnant, including your pathway home. The pathway is easily accessible by accepting the gifts, *and using the gifts for others.* This is the message of the community. Take these gifts; hold them tightly so that they become one with you. Then go and share them with the others. Through this action, goodness will prevail. God gives each of you these gifts to share with the circle of the souls. You will never be without the gifts because they are always available from God, always available from each other. They will be constantly surrounding you, like the cycle of life."

He touched my cheek lightly, like a warm breeze brushing my face. "Breathe in the gifts, thank God for giving them, and thank each other for sharing them. What you do not have will be supplied. Remember these words: The Lord will supply what you need. Then share this gift with your community. Greatness will occur on ordinary levels. Lives will change through this love. Walk in faith and think of the others. *You will never be forgotten, because you are within the circle of the souls, the circle of Christ."*

My heart pounded as he spoke those words. I repeated the sentences in my mind. *You will never be forgotten, because you are within the circle of the souls, the circle of Christ.*

"It's always so easy when you state it," I said slowly pondering my words. "But it's not always so simple. I have a friend whose child is a drug addict. As a mother she's struggling every day to find the gifts you speak about."

"The prayers of others, the angels, and the love of God will sustain her. She needs only to lift her face to the light.

"Remember," he continued. "I am only the messenger. God's love is the message. Soon you will take these messages, let them be known, and live them."

"*Try* to live them," I corrected him.

"Eventually, everyone will live them. Remember Christ's story

144

of the lost coin. Until all are found there will no true happiness. All must look for the coin and all must rejoice in its recovery. Amen," he concluded.

"Amen," I said, watching him ascend toward the cloudless sky. I wondered if I would ever be the person he wanted me to be.

"Your soul already is," he said, floating almost beyond my vision. "You need only to connect with it, and realize its potential, and there will be heaven on earth. Just turn toward God in prayer."

As the Archangel disappeared, I prayed silently and fervently.

Chapter Thirty

The Divinity of Christ

With my Bible in hand I looked for the parable of the lost coin. In the story a woman searches and searches for a coin she has lost. The coin is precious to her and she is miserable without it. When she finds it at last, everyone celebrates.

This time, unlike all the previous ones, I finally understood the story. It hit me like a ton of bricks. *We can't be truly happy until every one of us is with God.* I had heard the parable at least a dozen times before, but at last I understood it.

Closing the Bible, I found myself at the glass-enclosed bookcase. The Black Angel awaited me. His robes were bronzed and flowing, his ebony face washed in serenity. "Come," he said, motioning to me.

I took his hand and found myself being jostled on a busy city street. At first glimpse I would have guessed it to be New York City. Huddled over a subway grate lay an old woman, with long matted gray hair. A cardboard sign, fallen to her side, asked for money.

The woman didn't move. She could have been asleep, or dead.

The Black Angel and I stood there, watching people pass her by. They averted their eyes, picked up their pace, ignored her.

"What do you see?" the angel asked.

"A homeless woman," I said. "A sleeping homeless woman."

He shook his head. "Look with your soul. All of you look with your eyes and not your souls," he said almost harshly. "Please, look with your soul."

"I don't know *how* to look with my soul," I said, almost crying.

"Listen to your soul, and it will tell you how to view this woman."

I closed my eyes, trying to block out the sounds of the city, and trying to view the old woman differently. It was difficult.

"What have you been told?" he asked.

"That we are all one. When we see another, we see ourselves."

"Yes," he said with a nod. "So look into your soul and you will see this woman. Your soul contains the love and sight that you need for your pathway. Your soul is not blocked by the physical. It is the eyesight of the realm of the spiritual. When you look with your soul, you will feel her pain, and know her pain. With this comes compassion."

I shoved my hands into my coat pocket. "There are a lot of homeless people," I said, trying to explain my rationale. "And I know it sounds horrible, but if you give them all money, lots of it will go for alcohol or drugs."

"Did we ask you that? You always jump to conclusions. You are always ready to argue a point. Even though you understand things so much better, you still put up defenses."

I looked down at the cracked sidewalk.

"Christ said, `Whatsoever you do to the least of my brothers, you do unto me.'"

"Yes," I answered, remembering the verse.

"It is the circle of the souls. The divinity of Christ lies within her. As you treat her, so you treat Christ. As you treat the others, so you treat yourselves."

Staring at the woman, I wondered aloud, "How can I help all of these people?"

"Prayer," he responded. "Remember to pray, to be kind. We have told you many times. Remember that prayer results in action."

He made the sign of the cross over the woman's head, and we left the noisy city. Holding my hand tightly, he returned me to the bookstore. "Everyone you meet has a purpose in your life, on the pathway home. Prayer will move you along the path."

I felt the warm sun beat down through the crystal ceiling. "Sometimes it all seems so simple," I said, "and other times it seems impossible."

"Community is essential. You are all one. You are all connected. Therefore even those who feel alone must know that others are praying for them. Pray for strangers, pray for those in desperate need, pray for your enemies. As you pray for those whom you do not know, they in turn will pray for you. Eventually, all will be reunited with Christ."

Rubbing my forehead, I felt a pain rush through my temples.

"Do not block out what appears difficult," the Black Angel said.

I leaned against the wall. "But I do..."I mumbled, watching him disappear before my eyes. "I do." I felt so ignorant, so helpless.

As I stood there, the Voice began to speak. "You are never helpless when you face God. You are never lost when God is on your path. You are never forlorn when you turn toward the light. The light will be a beacon; it will guide you. And as this light carries you, you will pray for others. The results of prayer will be bountiful. The Lord is ever gracious, ever patient, ever loving, and waiting for each of you to return home to Him. Breathe in the breath of the Holy Spirit, absorb the wisdom, and unlock the spirit that lies within you. All your answers are within you; all the compassion and loving is within you. Your souls are perfect. God loves you unconditionally. Remember that you are to love your neighbors in the same vein. Pray for the others and that prayer will be returned to you."

I slid down to the floor of the bookstore. Looking up I noticed that the books surrounding me seemed infinite in number. They were encased in glass; I knew they were more lessons for me to learn.

The Voice continued. "The most important lesson is to love God and your neighbor. It is so simple...if only you would walk toward the Light."

Slumped in the corner, I wanted to cry out, "But where is the light switch?" Instead I said nothing.

"Do not wallow in doubt," the Voice said. "The knowledge has been sent to all of you to comfort you and bring you salvation. Each time doubt and anxiety arise, turn from it and remember that God's plan is a wondrous one. Amen."

"Amen."

I pulled myself up, and silently said a prayer for the homeless woman. It seemed such a small task—as if it would hardly have an effect.

"Have faith in the power of your prayers," the Voice said. "Have faith in them. All is possible through the Spirit."

Bowing my head, I made the sign of the cross.

Chapter Thirty-One

Prayer Results in Action

The February winds gusted outside my home, shaking the windowpanes with the fierceness of a New England winter. I held the phone to my ear, waiting for my friend to settle into her chair on the opposite end of the telephone line.

Only fifty years old, she had been diagnosed with a rare blood disease, one that few people had ever survived. Out of the blue, her body had stopped producing blood.

But her spirit never quit. Her attitude was one I will always admire. She was never bitter, always a heroine to her family, to her friends, and to me.

I wondered at my own ability to fight such a disease with courage, and I doubted I had the strength. Just a few days before I had found a lump on my neck, and until I saw the doctor each moment was filled with dread and apprehension. For 24 hours I had lived in some of the fear that engulfed my friend each day—and, quite truthfully, I wasn't very courageous. I was just lucky the lump was nothing.

I shifted the phone against my shoulder, and heard my friend's voice.

I was about to give her a brief meditation, along with a prayer, to help her visualize her disease.

We both shut off the call waiting, she closed her eyes, and I began to pray and visualize the orange-yellow platelets that she received in the hospital. I saw them like orange juice, full of nutrition and life, running through her body like the hot July sun, giving heat and energy to her system. As I guided her, I also prayed.

And then my friend began to cry.

I panicked. Who was I to help her? I had upset her, bothered her, said something disturbing. Gathering my voice, I asked, "Did I say something wrong?"

"No," she answered, "they're tears of joy."

After I hung up, the Archangel appeared to me.

My heart skipped a beat. A month had passed without any word from the angels. I had wondered if our visits were over, and hoped that they were not. The day before I had given a lecture on my experience to about sixty people at a church. Afterward some of the parishioners had approached me and told me that my talk was powerful. It was wonderful spreading such meaningful messages to a new group of people. For months I had shared the messages with a small group of friends, and now I felt it was moving outward...on its own.

The Archangel floated above me, his body seemingly held up by the dark sky. The stars turned beautiful colors. A deep lavender color dotted throughout the heavens. Alongside the Archangel was a bevy of angels.

"You are ready," he said.

"Ready for what?" I asked.

But he did not answer the question directly. "The message we have brought to you is the message of the circle of the souls, the message of community. Write this down," he continued. "God is everywhere and always listening to the souls. Tell everyone that we are constantly at their sides, waiting to whisper the words of divinity to their souls, waiting to perform acts of love. God is constantly with all of you. He looks forward to the circle of the souls reuniting in this unconditional love. As the woman in the Bible held fast to Christ's robes, do so also. Feel the energy of God, the energy of the Divine flow through you."

The sun was rising over the mammoth skyscrapers. For the first time I noticed that the sea was in the background. Why hadn't I seen that before? I wondered aloud.

"You, like the others, see only what you wish to see. Oftentimes you are blind to the beauty that surrounds you. I have been sent to the world to aid their sight, their vision," the Archangel said. "You are to open your eyes, open your souls to the beauty of God which is around you and within you."

I thanked him.

"Tell everyone to reach out to God, and to each other."

As I strained to see the ocean in the distance, I began telling the Archangel about the meditations I had done with my sick friend.

"Did I not tell you that prayer results in action?" he asked.

"Yes," I said slowly, mulling over the question. "But I thought you meant that the prayers would be answered by God's actions."

"Prayer will result in many actions," he said. "The actions of God, and the actions of the people. All will find that in doing this work, following His way is simple. You will walk in faith and prayers will be answered."

In many ways I knew the Archangel was correct. Before these messages began, I would never have asked this woman to pray with me, afraid she'd think I was a religious fanatic. Or afraid I would do it wrong, say something which would disturb her.

"This is the lesson," the Archangel said. "When you are in partnership with the Lord, all your actions come from Him."

I questioned him further about that.

"The Lord's gifts are perfect. If you work with the Lord, become one with this circle, all of your actions through prayer have magnificent results. No harm can come, no mistakes can be made."

"But I'm only human," I argued. "I could say something to upset my friend."

"But God is perfect Love. When you perform prayers, you are calling on His energy, His love. No mistakes can be made."

"Oh," I said, humbled.

"And your soul, perfect in the image of the Divine, connects with the Lord. It cries out to be with the Lord and with the others. All of this stresses the importance of the community. The message we bring to you is the message of the circle of the souls."

He took my hand, and although his touch was gentle, fear ran through my body. "Oh, no," I said, recognizing the expression in his eyes. "You're leaving me again, aren't you?"

"We are always with you, always with the others. It is not for me to remain visible while you absorb these lessons. I have delivered what is essential for this part of the journey. Others may come later, but you have much to study, much to pray. Now you have these messages to learn, to live with, and to utilize. It is essential that you work with these and understand the importance of community."

I curled my fingers around his.

"Be one with each other through prayer. This prayer will result in many actions. But as Christ came to reunite the Body, so you, too, must actively take a part for that purpose. Live the Way, follow the example, and hold fast the gifts which surround you."

My mind raced. I didn't want to lose my friend again, How could I live these messages? "Don't leave me again," I said, my teeth clenched.

His blue eyes appeared to be deep, bottomless pools. "The Spirit will listen to your prayers for wisdom. "You need only to accept these gifts and your vision will allow you to see the beauty. See with your soul, not your material eyes. And the world will take on a different appearance. You all will see sights beyond your imagination, sights of the beauty of God."

"Please," I pleaded. "Can't you stay?"

"We never leave you, nor does God. But you have now heard the messages. You are to pray, be one with each other and love each other. Celebrate the discovery of the lost coin. Ache for the return of the lost sheep, the prodigal sons and daughters. True happiness will never be achieved without unconditional love. And your soul understands this. Listen to the songs of your soul. Reunite with God and the circle of the souls."

He made the sign of the cross over my forehead. The heat of the dawn beat down on my body. In the distance the sea looked cool and inviting.

"You will see with new eyes," the Archangel said. "You will hear with new ears. All you need to do is seek God, and you will be with Him.

"Go," he said. "Seek God, practice the love we have spoken of. It will become like breath - you need it to survive. The soul is the life-giver of the body. Love is the energy of the journey. You cannot survive without this love. Breathe it in; experience it. Be one with it, with God, with each other."

He began to rise into the sky, his huge wings opening into an enormous wingspan. "Listen to the whispers. They will become louder and more deafening as you turn toward the Divine. All is available for the asking. All is available for the seeking." Slowly, as if praying over each stroke, the Archangel made the sign of the cross.

"Amen," I said weakly, knowing it was futile for me to cry out for him.

A bevy of angels filled the sky overhead. Many of them I recognized from prior visits: the Black Angel, the Asian Angel, the Turbaned Angel, and many smaller cherubs. They greeted the Archangel with soft, sweet, melodic songs. From my seat, I smiled.

I knew the Archangel had given me this sight. And just as importantly, I knew I would lose it.

But the true gift is the gift of Unity.

That, I hope, I shall never lose.

Just the Beginning